Table of C

The Sweet Wretchedness of Love

SIYA MANCI
A Double Date In Autumn

When falling in love

Love brings sorrow; love brings agitation, there's myrrh there's exhilaration. Be pre-emptive; be cautious when falling in love with someone.

Heartbreak Syndrome

Let's love one another with sincerity, honour and commitment . Do not play with someone's heart, he may die of a heartbreak. Heart strings, which are called tendons in biology- lose form during severe emotional trauma, whereby the heart ends up not being able to pump blood effectively . It is called a heart break syndrome.

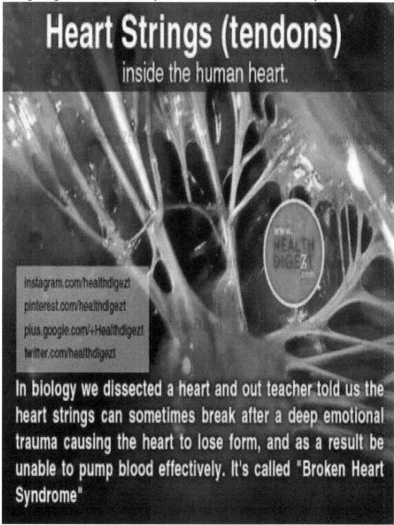

Heart Strings (tendons) inside the human heart.

instagram.com/healthdigezt
pinterest.com/healthdigezt
plus.google.com/+Healthdigezt
twitter.com/healthdigezt

In biology we dissected a heart and out teacher told us the heart strings can sometimes break after a deep emotional trauma causing the heart to lose form, and as a result be unable to pump blood effectively. It's called "Broken Heart Syndrome"

A Message On Love

Love is a magnificent and complex force that intertwines our lives, illuminating both our greatest joys and deepest heartbreaks. It has the power to uplift us to soaring heights or shatter us into a million pieces. In the pages that follow, we embark on a journey that explores the sweet wretchedness of love, where souls collide, desires entwine, and hearts are laid bare. Remember, in the realm of love, every triumph and every sorrow is a testament to our capacity to feel, to connect, and to endure. May this story remind you that even amidst the tumultuous waves of heartbreak, love's resilience shines through, guiding us towards healing, growth, and the endless possibilities of the human heart.

1 Acknowledgement:

I WOULD LIKE TO TAKE this moment to express my deepest gratitude and heartfelt thanks to all those who have supported and influenced me throughout the journey of creating "The Sweet Wretchedness of Love." Your unwavering belief in my talent and dedication to the craft of writing has been instrumental in bringing this book to life.

First and foremost, I would like to thank God, to express my deepest gratitude and heartfelt thanks to God, the Almighty, for blessing me with the gift of writing plays and poetry. It is through His guidance and inspiration that I have been able to bring "The Sweet Wretchedness of Love" to fruition. All of that in Jesus Christ name.

I am forever indebted to my late mother, Joyce Manci, for introducing me to the world of literature from a young age. Her nurturing presence, as she read children's books like "Three Bears," "Dumbo," and "Snow White" to me, sparked my imagination and instilled a deep love for storytelling.

When I was 15 years old, she made a librarian card for me to borrow books at UMzimkhulu Local Library. She encouraged me to explore new worlds through books, and her words of wisdom and endorsement to pursue writing and network with other writers have remained with me. She brought many books for me, when she was working at local pre-school- books like Dead Man's Fingers, to terrify me. In her last decade, she would bring me Shakespeare's plays, which inspired me to write plays in my mid to late teenage-hood. In her sickness, just before she died of kidney failure, in the mid-autumn of 2012-she motivated about my writing skills and that I should persist, endeavour to network with other local, national and international writers.

In the early stages of my writing journey, many individuals provided invaluable support and inspiration. I would like to express my gratitude to Sarah Goschen and her mother, Charleen Goschen, whose overwhelming support enabled me to write this book. Their generosity in providing me with a computer, the tool that became the gateway to my creative expression, is something I will forever cherish.

I would also like to acknowledge Barrie Lake and Dylan Cox for their unwavering love, care, and support during my time at Rhodes University in Grahamstown. Their presence in my life created an environment where my creativity could thrive, and their belief in my abilities fuelled my determination to pursue my passion for writing. I can never forget you-my dearest friend Xolani Xaba, you're my rock star.

I am grateful to Sipho Manci, Akhona Mboyi and Phumla Ngubo, who read my hand-written manuscript when I was still in primary and in high school. Their appreciation for my early writing inspired me to continue honing my craft. Their belief in my abilities as a storyteller gave me the confidence to pursue my dreams. I thank Miss Kholeka Ghana, who was my Life Orientation Educator at Clydesdale High School. She gave me guidance on how to write poems, short stories and plays. I would sit in her library, at school with other teachers reading books. She taught me how to navigate the library if there is book, I want to read. All of this back in 2009-2013.

A special mention and heartfelt thanks go to my neighbour, Nandipha Sosibo. In the early summer of 2023 and throughout the autumn of 2023, when I was going through a challenging phase emotionally and mentally-having a heartbreak, with other personal issues, she approached me with words of wisdom and encouragement. Nandipha reminded me of my past writings and urged me not to discard my talent. She saw potential in me and believed that writing could be my breakthrough, especially during times of financial constraints and joblessness. Without her intervention and unwavering support,

"The Sweet Wretchedness of Love" would not have come to fruition. I am forever grateful for her guidance and belief in me. During this transformative journey, I took the handwritten manuscript of the play, which I had left untouched since 2010-2011, and began the arduous task of typing it into a readable format on the computer.

There have been significant changes and modifications, including character development and an in-depth setting, from the original handwritten version. However, the core essence and themes of the play remain intact. Nandipha's encouragement and motivation were the driving forces behind this process, and I am indebted to her for her unwavering belief in my abilities.

To all those whose names I have mentioned and to those whose names may have been inadvertently omitted, please know that your support and encouragement have been pivotal in the creation of this book. Each one of you has played a significant role in shaping my journey as a writer, and I am deeply grateful for your impact.

In conclusion, I extend my heartfelt appreciation to everyone who has supported me along this writing and publishing process. Your unwavering belief in my talent, your encouragement, and your presence in my life have been invaluable. Together, we have brought "The Sweet Wretchedness of Love" to fruition. May our shared love for literature and storytelling continue to inspire us all.

With deepest gratitude,
SIYA MANCI

2 Author's Note:

Dear Reader,

I am thrilled to present to you "The Sweet Wretchedness of Love, "or what I like to call it; "A Double Date in Autumn". This play has been a labour of love, born from a deep passion for storytelling and a desire to explore the intricate tapestry of human emotions.

In crafting this tale, I aimed to delve into the complexities of love and its profound impact on our lives. Love is a force that can bring joy, but it can also lead to heartache and unexpected journeys. Through the characters and their intertwining relationships, I sought to portray the multifaceted nature of love and the various forms it can take.

"The Sweet Wretchedness of Love" is not just a story; it is an exploration of the human experience. It delves into themes of forgiveness, friendship, passion, and the challenges we face as we navigate the path to adulthood. I hope that within these pages, you will find moments of reflection and connection as you witness the characters' triumphs, struggles, and unexpected discoveries.

As an author, it is my greatest joy to transport readers into different worlds, allowing them to immerse themselves in the lives and journeys of my characters. It is my hope that through the vivid settings and compelling story, the play finds you greatly.

Regards,
SIYA MANCI
Email: g15m2868manci@outlook.com
Cell Number: +27 69 456 4200

3 The Rich Tapestry of Literary Genres: Exploring Plays, Novels, Shortly Stories, Poetry, and Folklore, With An

IN Depth Analysis On the Genres of Plays

3.1 Introduction:

LITERATURE ENCOMPASSES a vast array of genres that captivate readers and offer a diverse range of narratives. From plays to novels, short stories to poetry, and folklore to modern fiction, each genre brings its own unique essence and storytelling techniques. In this essay, we will delve into the variety of literary genres and their characteristics, exploring their impact on readers. We will particularly focus on the genre of plays, examining its distinct elements and discussing its significance in the realm of literature.

3.2 Variety of Literary Genres:

3.2.1 Plays:

PLAYS ARE LITERARY works designed for performance on a stage. They often incorporate dialogues, stage directions, and dramatic elements to convey stories and explore complex themes. Plays encompass various subgenres, such as tragedies, comedies, historical dramas, and experimental plays, each offering a unique theatrical experience (Heiman, 2018).

3.2.2 Novels:

NOVELS ARE LENGTHY works of fiction that typically explore intricate character development, intricate plots, and detailed settings. They can also be also of real historical events (Saule, N.,2009). Novels allow for in-depth exploration of various themes and genres, including romance, mystery, science fiction, and historical fiction (Watt, 2019).

3.2.3 Short Stories:

SHORT STORIES ARE CONCISE, self-contained narratives that focus on a single event or character. They often capture a moment of revelation or present a brief exploration of a particular theme or idea (Charters, 2017).

3.2.4 Poetry:

POETRY UTILIZES RHYTHM, meter, and figurative language to convey emotions, ideas, and experiences in a condensed and expressive manner. It encompasses various forms, including sonnets, haikus, odes, and free verse, allowing poets to experiment with structure and imagery (Abraham, 2020).

3.2.5 Folklore:

FOLKLORE CONSISTS OF traditional stories, songs, and customs passed down through generations within a specific culture or community. Folklore often serves as a reflection of societal beliefs, values, and traditions, preserving cultural heritage (Dundes, 2016).

3.3 In Depth Overview of Plays

3.3.1 Definition and Characteristics:

PLAYS ARE WRITTEN TO be performed on stage and rely on dialogue, actions, and theatrical elements to convey meaning. They often include stage directions to guide actors and directors. Plays typically explore complex themes, engage audiences through dramatic tension, and utilize various literary devices, such as monologues, soliloquies, and foreshadowing (Lupton, 2018).

3.3.2 Subgenres and Types:

PLAYWRIGHTS HAVE EXPERIMENTED with different subgenres and types of plays throughout history. Tragedy, comedy, tragicomedy, historical drama, and absurdism are among the notable subgenres that have emerged over time. Each subgenre presents a distinct set of conventions and allows playwrights to explore different aspects of human experience (Banham, 2014).

3.3.3 Significance and Impact:

PLAYS PROVIDE A UNIQUE medium for storytelling and social commentary. They engage both the intellectual and emotional faculties of audiences, allowing for thought-provoking experiences and discussions on various themes and societal issues. Plays can foster empathy, challenge societal norms, and offer a platform for critical examination of the human condition (Elam, 2017).

3.3.4 Conclusion:

LITERARY GENRES, SUCH as plays, novels, short stories, poetry, and folklore, offer readers a wide range of experiences and narratives. Each genre brings its own distinct elements, themes, and techniques, captivating.

3.4 Exploring the Rich Tapestry of Play Genres: A Journey Through Drama

3.4.1 Introduction:

WITHIN THE REALM OF literature, plays hold a significant place as they provide a unique and captivating medium for storytelling and artistic expression. The genre of plays, also known as drama, encompasses a diverse range of styles, themes, and narrative structures (Qangule, Z.S.,2008). This essay will delve into the various genres of plays, shedding light on their characteristics, historical significance, and enduring impact on the world of literature.

3.4.2 Tragedy:

TRAGEDY IS A GENRE of plays that explores the downfall of a noble or influential character, often resulting from a tragic flaw or external circumstances. (Nkohla,2014). These plays evoke intense emotions and often explore themes of fate, morality, and the human condition. Examples of classic tragedies include Shakespeare's "Hamlet" and Sophocles' "Oedipus Rex "(Hibbard,1987).

3.4.3 Comedy:

COMEDY IS A GENRE OF plays that aims to entertain and amuse audiences through humorous situations, witty dialogue, and light-hearted themes. Comedies often involve mistaken identities, romantic entanglements, and humorous misunderstandings. They provide a temporary escape from reality and promote laughter and joy. Examples of well-known comedies include Shakespeare's "A Midsummer Night's Dream" and "Twelfth Night "(Saunders, W.,2005) and Oscar Wilde's "The Importance of Being Earnest."

3.4.4 Historical Drama:

HISTORICAL DRAMA REFERS to plays that depict events, figures, or periods from history. These plays provide insight into historical contexts, exploring the lives and struggles of notable individuals or communities. According to Saunders, W (2005, p.6-14) historical dramas often combine elements of tragedy or comedy with factual events, fostering a deeper understanding of the past. William Shakespeare's Anthony and Cleopatra and Julius Caesar.

3.4.5 Absurdist:

ABSURDIST PLAYS CHALLENGE traditional narrative structures and present situations that defy logic and reason. They often highlight the existentialist philosophy of human existence in a chaotic and meaningless world. Absurdist plays provoke thought and reflection, forcing audiences to question the nature of reality and the absurdity of human actions (Hibbard, G.R, 1987.p.55); he gives notable examples include Shakespeare's Hamlet

3.4.6 Musical Theatre:

MUSICAL THEATRE COMBINES the elements of spoken dialogue, music, and dance to convey stories and emotions. These plays feature song and dance numbers that enhance the narrative and character development (Lammer, A et al.,1996. p.172-175).

3.4.7 Experimental Theatre:

EXPERIMENTAL THEATRE pushes the boundaries of traditional storytelling and challenges the audience's expectations. It explores unconventional forms, non-linear narratives, and avant-garde techniques to create unique and thought-provoking theatrical experiences (Gill.,1979-112-115). Experimental plays often tackle social and political issues and encourage active audience engagement. Notable experimental playwrights include Bertolt Brecht and Antonin Artaud.

3.4.8 Conclusion

THE GENRE OF PLAYS offers a vast landscape of storytelling, encompassing tragedy, comedy, historical drama, absurdist, musical theatre, and experimental forms. Each genre brings its own set of characteristics, themes, and artistic approaches, captivating audiences and provoking meaningful discussions. Through the centuries, plays have served as a powerful medium for self-reflection, social commentary, and artistic expression, making a lasting impact on the world of literature and theatre.

3.5 Exploring Love's Tapestry: "The Sweet Wretchedness of Love"

3.5.1 Introduction

"THE SWEET WRETCHEDNESS of Love" is a captivating play set in the vibrant towns of Cape Town. Love serves as the central theme, intertwining the lives of a diverse cast of characters as they navigate the complexities of romantic relationships, family dynamics, and friendship. This essay will delve into the themes, character dynamics, and narrative structure of your play, shedding light on its exploration of love's transformative power and the choices it presents.

3.5.2 Love as the Central Theme:

LOVE EMERGES AS THE primary theme in "The Sweet Wretchedness of Love." Through the experiences of the characters, the play delves into various aspects of love, including:

3.5.2.1 Romantic Love:

THE PLAY EXPLORES THE tumultuous journey of Bachelor, an 18-year-old on the precipice of adulthood, as he seeks his soulmate. His quest for love becomes entangled in a fierce rivalry with Casanova, creating a captivating dynamic filled with desire, passion, and competition.

3.5.2.2 Platonic Love:

BEYOND ROMANTIC LOVE, the play delves into the complexities of platonic relationships. Friendships are tested, and bonds are challenged as characters navigate loyalty, forgiveness, and the intricacies of their connections with one another.

3.5.2.3 Family Love:

FAMILY DYNAMICS PLAY a significant role in the exploration of love within the play. The challenges faced by Charles, Bachelor's friend, regarding his romantic issues with Cynthia and his father's infidelity, shed light on the complexities of familial love and its impact on personal relationships. Also, Valentine' endeavour to build his little family with Bachelor and Sharon his fiancée.

3.5.3 Character Dynamics:

"THE SWEET WRETCHEDNESS of Love" presents a rich tapestry of characters, each with their own desires, conflicts, and journeys. Some notable character dynamics include:

3.5.3.1 Bachelor and Casanova:

THE RIVALRY BETWEEN Bachelor and Casanova adds tension and complexity to the narrative. Their pursuit of love and affection from Precious showcases the contrasts in their personalities, highlighting the different approaches and philosophies they embody when it comes to matters of the heart.

3.5.3.2 *Charles and Cynthia:*

THE ROMANTIC ISSUES faced by Charles and Cynthia provide insight into the challenges and vulnerabilities of love. Their relationship becomes a catalyst for self-discovery, forgiveness, and the examination of the consequences of past actions. Cynthia indirectly endorses Precious to choose Casanova due to her insecurities and obscurities to have a friend of her boyfriend date her sister.

3.5.3.3 *Valentine and His Ex-Mistress:*

THE ENGAGEMENT OF BACHELOR'S brother, Valentine, is threatened by his past relationship with his ex-mistress. This subplot explores the complexities of love and loyalty, as well as the consequences of past decisions and the pursuit of personal happiness.

3.5.4 Narrative Structure:

"THE SWEET WRETCHEDNESS of Love" weaves together multiple storylines and character arcs, culminating in a climactic double date at the peak of autumn. This narrative structure allows for the exploration of various perspectives on love, creating a dynamic and interconnected web of relationships.

3.5.5 Conclusion:

"THE SWEET WRETCHEDNESS of Love" serves as a compelling exploration of love in its various forms. Through its examination of romantic, platonic, and familial relationships, the play delves into the transformative power of love and the choices it presents. The complex character dynamics and interwoven narratives offer a captivating and thought-provoking experience for both performers and audiences, reflecting the intricacies of the human heart.

4 The Sweet Wretchedness of Love:

An in Depth Analysis

4.1 The Plot

T he Sweet Wretchedness of Love" or what I like to call "The Double Date in Autumn", is a poignant and compelling play that delves into the life of an 18-year old boy Bachelor on a tumultuous journey to find love amidst complexities of adulthood as he works in family business, he becomes embroiled in hostile rivalry with Casanova a well-known player of same age.

The two are in a rival conflict over Precious, and their differences over societal norms and patterns pertaining to love, and role the role of men and women in society. Cynthia-Precious' sister fuels the conflict, ending in romantic issues with Charles a friend of Bachelor. As Charles grabbles with his romantic issues, he in heartache over his father's infidelity, meanwhile: Bachelor's brother Valentine 'engagement is threatened by his ex-mistress. In that very time, Bachelor goes on journey to find his soulmate, only to discover unwavering unprecedented love with Casanova.

The play culminates in a double date for Bachelor and Casanova at the peak of autumn.

4.2 Synopsis

THE DOUBLE DATE IN Autumn" is a captivating play that follows the journey of Bachelor, an 18-year-old boy who has recently graduated from high school. Set in the vibrant towns of Cape Town during the autumn season of 2010, the story explores the complexities of love, rivalry, and unexpected connections.

As Bachelor embarks on the tumultuous path to adulthood, he finds himself entangled in a fierce rivalry with Casanova, a well-known player, over the affections of Precious, who happens to be the sister of Cynthia, Charles' girlfriend. Charles is a close friend of Bachelor, adding another layer of complexity to their relationships.

Driven by his yearning for true love, Bachelor embarks on a transformative journey to find his soulmate. Along the way, he discovers that love takes many forms and can be both sweet and wretched. He encounters various characters who shape his perception of love, from the passionate and tumultuous relationships to the bonds of family and friendship.

The play explores themes of love from multiple angles, including marriage, erotic relationships, platonic love, sibling bonds, forgiveness, and the challenges of navigating adulthood. It delves into the complexities of human emotions, exposing the fragility of relationships and the choices we make in the pursuit of love.

As the story unfolds, readers are immersed in the vivid settings of Cape Town, including Green Point, Fish Hoek, Houtbay, Simon's Town, and Vredehoek. Against this backdrop, Bachelor's journey of self-discovery intertwines with the dawn of the 4th Industrial Revolution, reflecting the evolving dynamics of love and relationships in a rapidly changing world.

"The Sweet Wretchedness of Love" is a thought-provoking and emotionally charged play that invites audiences to reflect on their own experiences with love. It challenges conventional notions of romance and portrays the complexities, joys, and sorrows that love can bring. Prepare to be captivated by the interplay of characters, the vivid settings, and the exploration of love in all its beautiful and wretched forms.

4.3 Historical and Cultural Context:

"THE SWEET WRETCHEDNESS of Love" is set in the year 2010, during the vibrant Autumn season in South Africa. This particular time holds historical significance as it precedes the highly anticipated 2010 FIFA World Cup, which took place in South Africa during the winter months. The play captures the atmosphere of anticipation and excitement that swept across the nation as it prepared to host the prestigious global sporting event.

Against this backdrop, the play delves into the cultural dynamics of South Africa, with a particular focus on the white South African English culture. It explores the experiences, perspectives, and challenges faced by characters within this cultural context, while also shedding light on the racial dynamics and diverse socioeconomic classes present in the country.

The play portrays the complexities of racial relations, showcasing how different racial groups interact and navigate their relationships during this time. It delves into the nuances of privilege, prejudice, and the impact of historical legacies on present-day interactions.

Furthermore, "The Sweet Wretchedness of Love" captures the varying socioeconomic classes within South African society, ranging from the elite to the middle class and underclass. Through the portrayal of characters from different walks of life, the play highlights the disparities and tensions that exist within society, as well as the impact of social and economic factors on relationships and aspirations.

By incorporating these historical and cultural elements, the play provides a rich and nuanced portrayal of South African society in 2010. It offers insights into the intersecting dynamics of race, class, and culture, inviting audiences to contemplate the complexities of identity, societal expectations, and the ways in which these factors shape personal relationships and experiences.

4.4 Main Theme:

THE MAIN THEME OF "THE Sweet Wretchedness of Love" is love itself. Love is explored as a powerful and transformative force that influences the lives of the characters and drives their actions throughout the play. It encompasses various forms of love, from romantic and erotic relationships to familial bonds and friendships. The central theme of love weaves its way through the narrative, driving the plot and delving into the complexities of human emotions and connections.

Through intricacies of relationships, deceit, lust, riveting rivalries, and unprecedented connections: the play explores love through various sub themes of passion, manhood, sibling bond, arousal, eroticism, platonic love, entanglement, romance, and the transformative power of unexpected love and more.

4.4.1 Sub-Themes

4.4.1.1 Marriage and Commitment

THIS SUB-THEME DELVES into the institution of marriage and the challenges that arise within committed relationships. It explores the dynamics of loyalty, fidelity, and the struggles faced by couples as they navigate the complexities of love and long-term commitment. We witness opposing views on marriage between Sharon, who's engaged to Valentine and her postmodernist liberal feminist elder sister Nicole.

4.4.1.2 Romance

Romance is experimented by various characters in longing for attachment and sexual fulfilment. Characters are thirsty for intimacy, and endeavour for romantic experiment, to the point of hurting other people and themselves. While Bachelor is in intense emotional trauma longing for intimacy, Casanova is womanising for arousal to gratify his sexual urges. Some navigate romance through pick nicks, dates and hiking.

4.4.1.3 Sibling Bond

The play explores the intricate relationship between siblings, particularly through the characters of Precious and Cynthia. It delves into the complexities of sibling dynamics, highlighting the love, rivalry, and loyalty that can coexist within these bonds.

4.4.1.4 Teenagehood and Coming of Age

The sub-theme of Teenage-hood portrays the challenges and transitions that young adults like Bachelor face as they navigate the path to adulthood. It explores the exploration of identity, self-discovery, and the often-tumultuous nature of first loves and relationships.

4.4.1.5 Adulthood

The play navigates adulthood through Bachelor's inquest for love and career exploration, along with his rivalry Casanova who's questioning his futile lifestyle in his teenage-hood, and make his life intact. It also delves into the adultness of Valentine, as he's marrying Sharon in his early 30s as well his braveness and grooming Bachelor to the best man, with the aim to strengthen and grow his tiny family. At same time, inspiring to have such vast amount of wealth and riches.

4.4.1.6 Redemption and Forgiveness

Within the context of love, the sub-theme of forgiveness and redemption plays a significant role. It highlights the power of forgiveness in healing broken relationships, fostering personal growth, and finding redemption in the face of past mistakes and betrayals.

4.4.1.7 Friendship and Loyalty

The play explores the significance of friendship and the bonds of loyalty between characters. It delves into the complexities of friendships tested by love, rivalry, and conflicting desires, showcasing the strength and challenges of these connections.

4.4.1.8 Infidelity and Betrayal

This sub-theme examines the darker aspects of love, focusing on infidelity and betrayal. It delves into the consequences and repercussions of unfaithfulness, highlighting the emotional turmoil and damage caused by broken trust.

4.4.1.9 Lust and Temptation

Lust and temptation are explored as powerful forces that can disrupt relationships and challenge the characters' moral compasses. This sub-theme delves into the complexities of desire and the choices characters make when faced with temptation.

4.4.1.10 Deception and Secrets

There are deep past secrets, lies and deceits which escalates the intense conflict in the play, unfolding unprecedented love as they unravel.

"THE SWEET WRETCHEDNESS of Love" intertwines these sub-themes within the overarching exploration of love, providing a nuanced portrayal of the multifaceted nature of human relationships. Through these themes, the play invites audiences to reflect on the joys, challenges, and complexities of love in its various forms.

4.5 Main Character Profile

4.5.1 Bachelor: The Protagonist

BACHELOR IS THE PROTAGONIST of "The Sweet Wretchedness of Love." An 18-year-old boy who has recently graduated from high school, Bachelor embarks on a journey to find love and navigate the complexities of adulthood. He is characterized as a sincere and idealistic young man, driven by a deep desire to find his soulmate. Throughout the play, Bachelor experiences various challenges and rivalries, particularly with Casanova, as he learns valuable lessons about love, forgiveness, and self-discovery.

4.5.2 Casanova: The Antagonist

CASANOVA SERVES AS the primary rival to Bachelor in the pursuit of love. Known for his playboy reputation, Casanova is a charismatic and charming character who effortlessly attracts the attention of women. He represents the allure of temptation and the seductive power of his personality. Casanova's interactions with Bachelor highlight the contrasts between their approaches to love, ultimately leading to unexpected discoveries and personal growth for both characters.

4.5.3 Precious

PRECIOUS IS A KEY CHARACTER in the play and the object of affection for both Bachelor and Casanova. She is portrayed as an alluring and captivating woman who becomes entangled in the rivalry between the two men. Precious's character is faced with conflicts, particularly influenced by Cynthia's meddling, causing tension in her relationship with Charles, her boyfriend. Her journey throughout the play explores the complexities of love, loyalty, and the pursuit of personal happiness.

4.5.4 Cynthia

CYNTHIA PLAYS A PIVOTAL role in the plot, as her actions have consequences for both Precious and Charles. She is depicted as a manipulative character who meddles in Precious's affairs, causing conflicts and rifts in relationships. Cynthia's character embodies the themes of jealousy, betrayal, and the consequences of meddling in others' lives. Her actions serve as catalysts for several key events in the play.

4.5.5 Charles

CHARLES IS A FRIEND of Bachelor and a significant character in the story. He acts as a source of support and encouragement for Bachelor, helping him gain confidence in himself and his pursuit of love. Charles also grapples with personal challenges, including his father's infidelity, which fuels his understanding of love and loyalty. His relationship with Cynthia is tested, and he must navigate the complexities of trust and forgiveness.

4.5.6 Valentine

Valentine is Bachelor's brother, and their bond plays a crucial role in the play. As the older brother, Valentine mentors and grooms Bachelor with valuable business skills within the family company. His engagement is threatened by his ex-mistress, adding another layer of complexity to his character. Valentine's love and guidance shape Bachelor's journey, providing a supportive and guiding presence throughout the play.

4.5.7 Overview

EACH OF THESE CHARACTERS in "The Sweet Wretchedness of Love" brings their unique perspectives and challenges to the narrative, weaving a tapestry of emotions, relationships, and personal growth. Their interactions shape the plot and themes of the play, showcasing the complexities of love, friendship, loyalty, and the human experience.

4.6 Setting

4.6.1 Time

The Sweet Wretchedness of Love takes place in the vibrant and diverse city of Cape Town, South Africa, during the year 2010, specifically during the captivating Autumn season between early March and late May, 2010. The setting is carefully crafted to reflect not only the physical elements of the environment but also the cultural and technological context of the time.

THE PLAY PORTRAYS THE atmospheric changes of Autumn in Cape Town, showcasing the transformation of vegetation as the city transitions from the vibrant colours of summer to the more subdued hues of autumn. The climate and weather patterns of this season are vividly depicted, with the occasional cool breeze, scattered showers, and the warm golden light that bathes the city.

Within this backdrop, the setting captures the dawn of the Fourth Industrial Revolution, characterized by the emergence of evolving technologies and electronic devices. The presence of these modern elements is subtly woven into the play, reflecting the impact of technology on the characters' lives and aspirations. It serves as a backdrop for career path inspirations, showcasing the characters' interactions with digital platforms and their dreams of success in a rapidly changing world. Furthermore, it captures the emerging geopolitical shift of the BRICS: Brazil, Russia, India, China and South Africa in a complex global economic feud with the G7 countries, same time South Africa is joining the BRIC blocks to make BRICS.

The setting also captures the anticipation and excitement that precedes the FIFA 2010 World Cup, an iconic global sporting event hosted by South Africa. The energy and buzz surrounding the upcoming tournament are palpable, with references to the colourful banners, advertisements, and conversations about the games echoing throughout the city.

4.6.2 Place

The various towns of the City of Cape Town play an essential role in the setting, each with its distinct flavour and significance to the narrative. From within the Cape Town illuminating CBD, to Green Point that serves as the location of Bachelor's home and his family company, providing a glimpse into his personal life and career aspirations. Hout Bay portrays a luxurious and extravagant side, where Casanova resides in a prestigious hotel with his mother and owns an apartment, using his surroundings to allure and charm women.

FISH HOEK IS A PROMINENT setting in the play, as it is where Bachelor, Casanova, Charles, Cynthia, and Precious attended high school, before partying ways after high school graduation ceremonies. The town serves as a backdrop for their formative years, their friendships, and the intricate dynamics that shape their relationships. The scenes within Fish Hoek High School and False Bay College highlight the educational journey and the experiences shared by the characters during this pivotal time in their lives.

Lastly, Simon's Town and Vredehoek hold hidden secrets and a dark history that emerges throughout the play, shedding light on past events that have remained concealed. These locations serve as catalysts for revelations and pivotal moments in the characters' journeys, exposing the interconnectedness of their lives and the consequences of their actions.

Overall, the setting of "The Sweet Wretchedness of Love" intricately combines the natural beauty of Cape Town's Autumn season, the technological advancements of the Fourth Industrial Revolution, the anticipation of the FIFA World Cup, and the diverse neighbourhoods within the city. Through this vivid setting, the play captures the essence of time, place, and the interplay between personal stories and the larger societal context.

5 Dramatis Personae

1. BACHELOR
    2. Valentine (His brother)
    3. Casanova
    4. Helen (His Mother)
    5. Joshua (Bachelor and Valentine's Uncle)
    6. Charles (Bachelor's Friend)
    7. Andrews (Charles' father)
    8. Cynthia (Charles' girlfriend)
    9. Precious (Cynthia's sister)
    10. Marry (Andrews' Colleague and mistress)
    11. Rose (Casanova's girlfriend)
    12. Ntombi (Casanova's Girlfriend).
    13. Paul (Andrews' friend; Rose and Max's father)
    14. Max (Valentine's friend).
    15. Leah (Valentines' ex-girlfriend)
    16. Delilah (Leah's mother)
    17. Sylvia (receptionist at Helen's Hotel)
    18. Pretty (Co-worker at Helen's Hotel).
    19. Ruth (Precious' class mate)
    20. Ndalo (Casanova's friend)

21. Sithabile
23. Matthew
24. Grace
25. Candies
26.Mrs Peterson
27.Learners
28.Students
29.Prisoner
30. Police

6 Summary

6.1 Overview of the Plot, setting, protagonist, antagonist and tritagonist

6.1.1 The Plot

Bachelor, an 18-year-old who has just graduated high school, is struggling to find love and navigate adulthood while working in the family business. He becomes embroiled in a rivalry with Casanova, a well-known player, over Precious, the sister of Cynthia, who is Charles' girlfriend: Charles is a friend of Bachelor. As the two compete for Precious's attention, Bachelor goes on a journey to find his soul mate and eventually discovers unexpected love with Casanova. Meanwhile, Bachelor's friend Charles grapples with his own romantic issues and his father's infidelity, while Bachelor's brother Valentine's engagement is threatened by his ex-mistress. The play culminates in a double date for Bachelor and Casanova at the peak of autumn.

6.1.2 Theme

Love is the main theme of "The Double Date in Autumn," explored through various sub-themes such as marriage, erotic relationships, platonic love, family, sibling bonds, manhood, teenage hood, brotherhood, adulthood, infidelity, treacherousness, envy, sexism, friendship, forgiveness, and lust. The play examines how love can take unexpected forms and can bring people together despite their differences and past conflicts.

6.1.3 Place

"The Double Date in Autumn" takes place in various locations in Cape Town, including Green Point, Fish Hoek, Hout Bay, and Vredehoek, during the autumn season of 2010; spanning from 115 March to late May, also; it is occurring at the dawn of the Fourth Industrial Revolution-furthermore, it is just prior to the 2020 FIFA World Cup.

6.1.4 The Protagonist

The protagonist of the play is Bachelor, an 18-year-old who is struggling to find love and navigate adulthood while working in his family's business. Bachelor is portrayed as a sensitive, introspective character who is grappling with low self-esteem and societal pressure to conform to certain standards of masculinity. His journey to find love and acceptance drives the plot of the play.

6.1.5 The Antagonist

The antagonist of the play is Casanova, a well-known player who has dated many girls from high school and is full of pride and ego. Casanova is portrayed as a manipulative character who enjoys the attention and power that comes with being a ladies' man, endorsed by patriarchy, heteronormativity and sexism. His rivalry with Bachelor over Precious is the main source of conflict in the play.

6.1.6 Cynthia and Ndalo's Role

Cynthia is Bachelor's friend who is dating Charles, a closest friend of Bachelor. Cynthia endorses her sister Precious to choose Casanova over Bachelor, which fuels the conflict between Bachelor and Casanova: and also; causes tension between Cynthia and Charles.

Ndalo is a friend of Casanova who bad-mouths Bachelor to Casanova and twists everything Bachelor says in a negative way, which further stokes Casanova's animosity towards Bachelor. Cynthia and Ndalo's actions contribute to the escalating conflict between Bachelor and Casanova, ultimately leading to their showdown and unexpected love for each other.

7 The Sweet Wretchedness Love

A Double Date in Autumn

7.1 Act One
7.1.1 Scene One

(Green Point, Cape Town, an affluent suburb on the Atlantic Seaboard of Cape Town, South Africa, located to the northwest of the central business district. It is a popular residential area for young professionals and the Cape Town gay and lesbian community, alongside the gay village of De Waterkant; with a mid-rise apartment and mixed-use developments that have gone up in recent years. Somerset Road forms the principal thoroughfare lined by restaurants, café, delis, boutiques and nightclubs.
The Braemar Estate includes a few dozen properties that are restricted to single dwellings only, within the boundaries of Green Point
In a peaceful olive grove on a sunny afternoon in the afternoon in autumn. An 18-year-old boy, named Bachelor, sits alone under a tall tree. He seems to be lost in thought, deep in contemplation).

Bachelor: *(Speaking to himself.)* I wonder why life is full of intricacies and derailing for me; I have such a bad social life. People see me as a nerd, and hardly anyone wants to associate himself with such a person. *(He pauses for a moment, looking up at the rustling in the wind.)*

(Bachelor Continues): I'm at the doorstep of adulthood now, yet I do not have a girlfriend. All my friends and acquaintances in some sort of relationships- have girlfriends to boyfriends, they talk about them all the time, post themselves on social media; go out on dates, and here I am alone under this tree.

(Confused, he gazes up at the sky, at birds flying above.): I do not know what sex is like or cuddling for that matter. I cannot imagine myself drinking, smoking and partying: moreover, I am shamed for

that. I am seen as a fool sometimes, peer pressured to be as 21st century teen like others.

Bachelor: *(Birds are flying and singing across the trees.)* Hmmm... *(He is thinking, nods, sighs, takes a sip from a guava juice and eats some grapes. He continues reading for some moments and looks up at the tree.)*

Bachelor: Even Charles, my friend; has someone in his life... a girlfriend whom he delights with. When it comes to me, I just have this fear. I am so introverted though I enjoy being g solitude, and sometimes loneliness kills me.

Bachelor: *(Muttering):* In all, why does all this matter if I have a girlfriend or not? To appease people and feel embraced?

(He takes a deep breath to sort out his thoughts): Then there is that trash Casanova. I cannot comprehend why these girls are so lured into him.

Bachelor :(*contemplating):* Is it because of his countenance, or does his slippery tongue work for him?

Bachelor: *(Disheartened):* If I want to approach a girl, I tremble. I need to be a man. Had I had a girlfriend, I would bring her here, cuddle, and have some fun. I once tried to hook up with Ntombi, *(inflamed.)* but she rejected me and went into that treacherous self-ingrained Casanova.

Bachelor :(*He looks down, fidgeting with his hands):* When my brother Valentine asks me about my sexual relationship; I always give him indirect answers. Maybe if my father was still alive, my life would have been different. It's a pity I can't even recall how they looked like when they died.

Bachelor :(*Concluding):* Well... let me keep on reading, otherwise, I am going to distress myself with things that cannot be changed. I need to stop worrying about what others think. I need to focus on myself and my happiness. Maybe one day I shall find someone who truly loves me for who am I. As for now; I need to be content with myself and my own company. *Exit*

7.1.2 Scene Two

(A beach in Hout Bay, Cape Town: In the early afternoon, the weather is sunny and warm, and the sound of waves crashing on the shore can be heard in the background. People are swimming, and some are basking in the sun-rocky hills surrounding the beach. Casanova, an 18-year-old boy, is sitting under an umbrella on the shore, gazing out at the ocean. The weather is sunny and warm, and the sound of waves crashing on the shore can be heard in the background. Casanova looks confident and smug as he begins to speak.)

CASANOVA: *(speaking to himself.)* Ah, what a beautiful day. The sun is shining, the waters are crystal clear, and the beach is filled with beautiful women.

(He leans back in his chair, crossing his arms, and smirks to himself.)

Casanova: *(continuing.)* I've had so many girls, it's almost too easy. They just can't resist me. I know exactly what to say and how to say it. It's a gift, *(He pauses for a moment, looking out at the water, before continuing.)*

Casanova: But not everyone has it like me. Take Bachelor, for example. We went to high school together, and he was always too afraid to approach girls. He would stutter and stumble over his words, and it was painful to watch.

(He shakes his head in disgust.)

Casanova: *(**continuing**.)* But not me. I know exactly what to do. I'm smooth, I'm confident, and I always get what I want. And these girls, they just can't get enough of me.

(He smiles to himself, clearly enjoying the attention.)

Casanova: (*continuing.*) I just wish more guys were like me. It's not that hard, you just have to be bold and confident. Girls love that kind of thing. It's like they can smell it on you or something. Even Mr. Andrews-Charles' father is doing this-but then; when you reach that age; you shouldn't be committing infidelity.

(*He leans forward, his eyes gleaming with confidence and pride.*)

Casanova: (*continuing.*) Yes, being a player is a gift. And these girls, they're lucky to have me, as for Bachelor; he needs to learn from me and stop being too sensitively and insecure around women for it's easy to lure them. Why can't he be like me, or any other guy that knows how to prey on girls. His friend Charles a girlfriend for that matter, why can't he?

(*Gazing at the raging waters from the sea.*)

Casanova: (*Boasting.*) Life is so nice, so wonderful. I am the most popular guy around. All the girls love my charm, my countenance, my popularity, and my excellence in rugby. As much as it may sound immoral, I enjoy playing around with girls.

(*He chuckles to himself, looking out at the water once again.*)

Casanova: (*concluding.*) But for now, I'll just sit here and bask in my glory. The world is my playground, and these girls, they're just the icing on the cake.

(*Ntombi Enters, she's wearing a black swimming costume, slanderous by stature; she is carrying some milkshake*).

Ntombi: Ndazi uthetha naban...

Casanova: Ntombi! (*He frightens.*)

Ntombi: Whom were you speaking to?

Casanova: No one.

Ntombi: I know, you seemed to be smiling and giggling.

Casanova: Nothing, nothing of your concern. I was just talking with myself. It's not necessary.

Ntombi: (disgruntled.) Nothing of my concern? That's so cold!

Casanova: I cannot trust you with this, it shall get me into trouble.

Ntombi: Dude! (She sits.) Tell me kaloku.

Casanova: Do not dare tell anyone...

Ntombi: I shall not.

Casanova: Andrews is having an affair while his wife is away.

Ntombi: *(amused.)* What! Do you mean Andrews, the commerce H.O.D at Fish Hoek High School?

Casanova: Yes, the one and only.

Ntombi: *(Chuckles.)* Shame...I feel sorry for his wife. Where did you get this? When has it been happening?

Casanova: You know that Mrs Andrews is a sports journalist, so she is hardly around these days since she is all over the country in preparation for the 2010 FIFA world cup. So, he has been busy with Marry, he even bought her an Apple iPad. I saw him giving her at Helen's Hotel, right behind me.

Ntombi: *(surprised.)* Wow! That may cost around $499.00, which is equivalent to R 4000.00 to R 4 500.00. What is worse, she is a colleague of Mr Andrews; she knows Mrs Andrews, and Mrs Andrews knows her. I feel sorry for Charles; imagine finding out that your father has been cheating on your mother with a colleague!

Casanova: Do not dare tell him!

Ntombi: How did you get to know all of this?

Casanova: Come on, have you not been noticing them? Everybody knows how close they are, and very cosy when they are together. I have even seen them myself.

Ntombi: Where?

Casanova: In places like restaurants, at college, and here in Hout Bay, at my mother's hotel.

Ntombi: Men are so cruel.

Casanova: Not all of us. *(Smiling).* I am the sweetest you'll ever meet. *(They laugh, and ended up cuddling and kissing).* I love you.

Ntombi: I love you too.

Exeunt

7.1.3 Scene Three

(Kirstenbosch National Botanical Gardens. Nestled at the eastern foot of Table Mountain in Cape Town. Enter Charles and Cynthia; Charles is playing a Justin Bieber song; Baby, through his Nokia Express Music Cell phone. They're both singing to the song. It is so loud.)

Cynthia: This cell phone is so loud, it's as if you're playing home theatre. It reminds me of Haifa back in the 1990s and early 2000s.

Charles: True indeed, and it's the most trending mobile cell phone now. It is replacing Samsung v 360 and Samsung E250, furthermore; it's strong, even if it falls, it doesn't break.

Cynthia: Precious wants it, but our mother won't have it, as she still possesses a Samsung E250 I.

Charles: Lol. *(He laughs).* Which reminds me of something. Where is she?

Cynthia: She is at home.

Charles: How is she? She and Bachelor, what's app with them?? Are they going to make it?

Cynthia: *(Clinched.)* Precious would never date that one. Your friend is a sort of a loser. He's too uptight, and such a nerd.

Charles: Do not speak like that about him! He is just different. Why are you saying she would not dare hook up with him?

Cynthia: She seems to be into Playboy.

Charles : *(Exclaimed.)* Yhooo! What? How can you allow her to be captured by that manipulator, Casanova? That dude is up to no good.

Cynthia: They aren't item yet, it's just my suspicions- and Casanova hasn't said anything openly but one can spot he's into her.

Charles: What makes you think then that Bachelor has no chance?

Cynthia: He seems gay. His personality isn't robust, and he is a bit sluggard and flamboyant, furthermore, he's never dated any girl.

Charles: Stop making presumptions about people's personalities. Personality is too complex to just simplify it and justify someone's supposedly sexual orientation. Even if he is, he might still be trying to find himself and confused. There is nothing wrong with being gay, for that matter.

Cynthia: Wow! You are wise beyond your countenance. Okay, I know Casanova is not good for her, but who tells her what to do? When Precious wants something, she does it. She is a mere 17-year-old, and I am 19, but I'm not hard-headed and determinant as <u>she</u> is: which is why, I have decided to let her make her own decisions and her own mistakes. *(She sighs.)* ... Enough about her and Bachelor. Let's focus on us, babe.

Charles: *(He switches the music off from the cell phone.)* How are you feeling? *(He embraces her.)*

Cynthia: I couldn't be more agitated; I feel elated when I am with you. You're exquisite, and pleasant to stare; gladness is in me, you've captivated my heart.

Charles: I love you, I feel you in my inner being. *(He kisses her).*

Cynthia: I love you too. You wash my heart, my soul. When I am with you, I feel so alleviated *(They embrace and kiss.)* I can't wait for our graduation; we shall be dazzling as stars.

Charles: You are so fast, you are thinking about graduation at this time, we've not even accomplished the first semester of our tuition.

Cynthia: I have always longed for it. I cannot wait. I want to be the lady in red.

Charles: Wow. *(He kisses her.)* You just reminded me of one of my favourite songs. *(He plays the song, Lady in Red.)* I'll be wearing a black or royal navy suit.

Exeunt

7.1.4 Scene Four

(Green Point, a family home, Valentine and Sharon.)

Sharon: Wow, you hand is amazing; I wonder why you did not become a chef.

Valentine: I had been thinking of starting my show, maybe making a proposal with SABC 3 or e-TV to show my astounding cooking expertise. It's just the means I do not have.

Sharon: Well, you can start with a YouTube channel. That can be a start.

Valentine: Really?

Sharon: Yea, a lot of people are doing that these days; though it is slight in South Africa but the USA and rest of the first world countries, it's prominent. I'd like some wine...

Valentine: Cool. *(He opens it and pours for them both.)* Take a sip, fresh from the Garden Route, brought it specially for you, my love my strength. *(He kisses her.)*

Sharon: Hmm, you're so sweet. I love you. *(they embrace, he brushes her by the waist, while she's wrapping her arms over his shoulders.)*

Valentine: I love you more. I couldn't be happier than being with you, my love. Spending my life with you is my zeal, to grow and age together.

Sharon: I'd be glad. There is none other than you. I am so happy, my career is going well in a male-dominated law firm industry; I have a beautifully lovable astounding man, a car and my apartment. I am well settled... God has truly blessed me.

Valentine: So, what's your next case about?

Sharon: You can't believe I'll be standing for a man who is about to lose half of his wealth, since he married in a community of property. They've only been married for a year, imagine!

Valentine: (Acclimated.) What! Who does that? She's a gold digger like Xhosa women.

(They refrain from embracing)

Sharon: (*laughs.*) That's a bit extreme, you can't say that!

Valentine: Apologies, I am being prejudice here. I blame the media and television series for portraying such bizarre tribalism. So, what's your take on this case?

Sharon: I cannot comprehend why people do not thoroughly discuss before signing a piece of paper, even before you propose, marriage is something that should be your main discussion if you intend to marry each other, there are so many intricacies that come with it; though this woman might be seen as a gold digger, marriage is suppressive to the woman in many cases.

Valentine: So, what do you think? Are you against it?

Sharon: Not really, I am not a hard-core third-wave feminist. Marriage has its own obscurities, pitfalls and brighter side as well. The most important question should be; why do you want to marry? Are you marrying because of status, beauty, money, power, leverage, or wealth? If it is one of those do not marry. Moreover, if it's about love, comfort, completeness, stability and security, then yea... nevertheless; I do not think it's that important to sign a piece of paper, the state should stay out of marriages. You may have a wedding, or marry in a church by a pastor to be joined by God. We would even avoid these marriage court cases about LGBT, Islamic marriage, customary, civil or whatever else. The State should stay out of an individual's marriage.

Valentine: You have a point there, but then not signing anything would be like you do not trust each other.

Sharon: On that case, you may sign, but then do a preen-up if you do not want to be in this mess.

Valentine: True indeed, marriage has its costs and benefits; on one side; you do not want to be lonely when you are old, for after all pleasure: beauty shall decay, weariness shall immerge, and futility shall come. You need someone on your side in your old age, someone you ought to build trust with as you are ageing nevertheless; as you have mentioned; some are opportunists. They see it as their ticket to wealth. However, in whatever way may be: I believe you and I are meant to be together, and we've spoken about this many times and comprehended each other's stance. I love you. *(He kisses her.)*

Sharon: I love you too dear, I feel such intriguing affection when I'm with you: deep in my heart; up in my mind, you dwell. When I am with you, I feel like I am being lifted by the waves of the ocean. *(They kiss and embrace.)*

(Bachelor enters, he clears throat.)

Valentine: Hey bro, where have you been?

Bachelor: I was in the garden.

Valentine: You were here all this time?

Bachelor: Yes.

Valentine: Please do not forget to come to my office tomorrow. I want you to assist me with something; the company shipping some 23 tonnes of wine to Portugal.

Bachelor: Cool, I shall be there.

Valentine: I want you to be hands-on with the company now; I doubt this education system teaches you anything valuable for post-matric life.

Bachelor: True indeed, our education system is nonsense. It was designed back in the 18th century at the dawn of the industrial revolution, and it's embedded in memorisation of the text instead of practicality. I'd say even Mediaeval education was more hands on-just look at the astounding mesmerising everlasting architecture of the High Middle Ages.

Sharon: What is worse, South Africa inherited the British Victorian England kind of education, whereby education was a sort of leisure for the upper class. It is not like the practical and productive kind of education in China, Korea, Japan, and Germany. Come sit, we were just celebrating my birthday today.

Bachelor: Happy birthday. What is the date today?

Sharon: It's the 15th of March, I am officially 30 years old. I am so glad to have left in my 20s. We even have a full moon tonight. I could not even celebrate my birthday well since it is Monday today.

Bachelor: Why didn't you go out? Try it on Human Rights DAY-the 21st of March; or on the quarter moon on Monday next week, since the holiday falls on Sunday, and we shall observe it on the 22nd. (*He sits down and takes some snacks and juice.*) It's also my birthday.

Sharon: Really?

Bachelor: Yes. Next week is the March equinox; the sub-sola point shall leave the Southern Hemisphere and cross the celestial equator, heading northward as seen from Earth, also; it will be marking the beginning of astronomical autumn.

Sharon: Oh, yea I see. I once heard in class about the autumnal equinox which occurs around 21st March: but then, when you get to this age, you shall see. Going out and hanging around a lot of people turns you off. So, you prefer indoors.

Bachelor: No wonder Valentine has been partying less for the past two years. He was so gallivanting in his twenties.

Valentine: Yea, I have reached maturity, but they say life begins at 40. Who knows? I might be wild again. (*They laugh.*)

Sharon: No way, you can't be grooving with the 2000s at that age, they'll be in their late teenage hood or early twenties.

Valentine: I guess you are right.

Exeunt

7.1.5 Scene five

(The following day, enter Andrews and his son Charles... a setting in Fish Hoek, a Family House.)

Charles: When is mother coming back?

Andrews: I do not know hey, I was hoping to hear from you. Have not spoken to her?

Charles: Dad, she is your wife.

Andrews: I do not know... *(He sits, brushes his head, and folds his arms).* She is always busy; you know she is a journalist; she works for ENCA.

Charles: I might be young, but I sense some sort of lack of communication between you, too. A text would do. We even have Mix-It these days.

Andrews: What's that?

Charles: It's the most popular network in Africa currently.

Andrews: I think I might have heard about it. I know Facebook and Twitter though; but your mother is not a Facebook person, she is more on Twitter since she is communicating for a larger, broad and range audience. However, I am still more into the traditional way of commutation; regular calls and SMS or text message. These social media platforms are for you- millennials.

Charles: Well... you should change, you adapt and stop being technophobic. There is even WhatsApp now, very efficient in communication. it allows users to send text and voice messages; makes voice and video calls, and share images, documents, user locations, and other content for smart phones like yours. WhatsApp's client application runs on mobile devices, and can be accessed from computers. The service just requires cellular mobile telephone number. This disconnection between you and mother; displeases me. If not fixed, it's going to fracture your relationship or pave a way for a serpent to sneak in between you two.

Andrews: *(He is intense and shivering).* You are wise, son, but do not worry, nothing like that shall happen.

(A Bell rings).

Charles: Let me go see. *(He goes and opens, and Marry budges in, she had thought it was Andrews opening the door.)*

Marry: Hey, honey. *(She is shocked, there is an awkward moment.)*

Marry: *(She mumbles and stutters.)* I just came here to bring to some files and fetch an SBA.

Charles: Okay, he is inside. *(She gets in, and Andrews is shivering.)* Good afternoon, what brings you here?

Charles: *(He checks at the time.)* Let me go now. I have somewhere to go. *(He takes some car keys and leaves.)*

Andrews: Marry, you cannot just budge in here at any given time. You are going to get us caught.

Marry: Well... sorry. But you said I can come to you whenever I please, since Charles is in college, and always busy with surfing. He goes to the CBD now and then also.

Andrews: We need to change a strategy, otherwise, hell shall break loose.

Marry: Okay then, we need to find a safe place; I do not want to break anyone's marriage.

Andrews: And I sense my son is suspicious.

Marry: Why?

Andrews: Never mind. Come here. *(He opens his arms and embraces her.)*

Marry: I have missed you.

Andrews: I have missed you more. *(They kiss.)* I love you.

Marry: Please do not fool me, let us just be sex buddies and not mention that word.

Andrews: *(He laughs.)* You tell me that; you don't feel anything?

Marry: I do, I feel you. I feel you in my inner being in my veins.

Andrews: I feel you in the deepness of my body. *(They embrace and kiss.)*

Exeunt

7.1.6 Scene Six

(Devil's Peak: part of the mountainous backdrop to Cape Town, South Africa, looking at Table Mountain from the city centre; While when seeing the standard picture postcard view of the mountain, the skyline is from left to right: the spire of Devil's Peak, the flat mesa of Table Mountain, the dome of Lion's Head and Signal Hill.
Exposed to wind and mist. They cover the northern slopes overlooking the city centre in typical Cape Peninsula Shale Fynbos; which are hotter and prone to frequent fires, and as a result, the vegetation is low.
The slopes on the Southern Suburbs side, however, are naturally wetter; with some dense afro-montane forests: there are some indigenous animals such as porcupines, caracals, small grey mongoose, rock hyraxes and many species of birds.
The upper, rocky parts of Devil's Peak, Table Mountain and Lion's Head consist of a hard, uniform and resistant sandstone; the tough sandstone rests conformably upon a basal shale, which in turn lies uncomfortably upon a basement of older rocks
In the afternoon, the sun is about to set; enters Casanova)

Casanova: Wow, it's so nice being here, the wind blows so nicely, marvellous view of the CBD, Table Bay, Green Point and beaches around. *(Bachelor enters.)* You! What brings you here?

Bachelor: I am hiking. This is a public place. What's your story?

Casanova: You! Why do you always try to ruin things for me? Are you jealous?

Bachelor: Jealous about what?

Casanova: That all the girls are into me, even when we were in high school; and you are such a loser.

Bachelor: You are a bastard Casanova-a self-ingrained person, and a manipulative self-aggrandised fool! Who the hell do you think you are? Do you think jumping from this woman to the other makes you a better man?

Casanova: I do not point anyone with a gun, I simply talk and things happen. I am unlike you, who is a nerd, always intense, lonely and too serious. I still cannot comprehend why you get along with Charles that much. You do not even do boys' stuff. I even doubt your sexual orientation.

Bachelor: Do not dare insult me with your patriarchal toxic masculinity tendencies. What I do with my time in my life has nothing to do with my sexual orientation. You are such a dog dude! I feel sorry for Ntombi and these other girls for falling for such a vile individual like you.

(Charles enters.)

Charles: Terry a little! What's wrong with both of you? Why are you always at each other's throats? Fighting like cats and dogs? Grow up and stop this nonsense. You Casanova, I know how forward you are. Stop peaking on Bachelor. Differing from you does not make him less of a man.

Casanova: *(In a mockery, sarcastic way)* Okay, let me go. Delight in love with your friend

Charles: What did you say?

Casanova: Never Mind. *(He goes, gets inside a car and drives away.)*

Bachelor: I really cannot stand that piece of crap.

Charles: It's funny how much you have so much resemblance, but you cannot stand each other.

Bachelor: O please, I wish people can stop saying that. Some have even said there is a sliver of common personality traits.

Charles: O yes, the way you smile and the way you burst when in anger.

Bachelor: O please, let's stop talking about that arrogant, self-ingrained dude!

Charles: So, how are things between you and Precious?

Bachelor: Time, will tell. I'll wait for her to get back to me.

Charles: Bro, no woman would that! You got to have to chase her, show you are enthusiastic about her.

Bachelor: I am not that kind of person. I give people space, and I can't be forcing someone who is not interested in me.

Charles: Do you see? That is why it shall be inconvenient for you to fall in love. You need to get out of your comfort zone and take charge.

Bachelor: So, I must change who I am?

Charles: Not that you must change per se, but how you interact and blend with people.

Bachelor: Oh, I see. Wait... what brings you here?

Charles: I could not reach you through a call, neither Facebook nor mix it; I suspected I'd find you here, since you adore hiking and enjoy this scenery. Let's go surfing. I'll drive you home when we are done.

Bachelor: Cool, we can go.

Exeunt

7.1.7 Scene Seven

(Fish Hoek, 11th Avenue in the evening, a setting in a family house. Enter Sharon and Nicole, they are preparing for supper in the kitchen.)

Nicole: What are we making today, sister?

    Sharon: Just a mutton skew, with pap and some green vegetables.

Nicole: Oh wow, I love mutton. *(She opens the refrigerator and grabs some nectar.)* So how was work?

Sharon: It was well, nothing new or that interesting.

Nicole: You are going to burn the pot *(loudly)*.

Sharon: Oh... *(She goes and stirs.)*

Nicole: You seem to be somewhere else though, blousing.

Sharon: You know... *(She puts down the knife and leans onto the table.)* I was speaking to Valentine.

Nicole: Yea?

Sharon: We were just speaking about general instincts, about what we desire, just mere stuff usually that couples ought to discuss.

Nicole: What about?

Sharon: A lot, one that stood out to me, was marriage.

Nicole: Did he propose?

Sharon: No. It was just about how we view marriage. Is marriage worth it today or not? And the costs and benefits of marriage.

Nicole: What are your thoughts? You have been together for a decade now. Started the millennium as a couple when we shot crickets at 12 midnight entering the 2000s; cuddling and kissing each other.

Sharon: O that moment, it feels like yesterday. We met on that New Year's Eve, 31 December 1999; it was love at first sight: came 12

O'clock; I felt like I was being moved by the waves. That was our first kiss. I was 20, and he was 23.

Nicole: And I did not like him at first. I thought he just wanted to chow you on New Year's Eve New to New Year's Day. *(She smiles.)* We were at the beach in Hout Bay. It took me years, to adore him. I started to respect and honour your relationship with him by the mid-2000s.

Sharon: I remember when you took us to a luncheon. Back in 2005, I had just finished my LLB degree at Rhodes University in Grahamstown the previous year.

Nicole: Yea. Valentine and you have been through a lot; had your ups and downs. You fought: you broke up, and you went back together. As of now, understand each other's personalities so well. He is such a protective man; he is like a leopard, and he ambushes for an opportunity and brings fruitfulness to it. That man loves you.

Sharon: I have grown with him; reached maturity with him. There is no other man I shall find other than him. If he were to ask me to marry him, I would say yes instantly.

Nicole: You see. But be careful, you are a lawyer, and marriage is another mess and a long journey. You marry someone, everything is fine on the wedding day, and then there comes marriage. Endure, and love your partner when he shows his true colours. Love him while you say I want to kill him; but then look at him and say, I love this man, and there is none other than him.

Sharon: True indeed. So, when are you getting married? You've passed the youth stage.

Nicole: Marriage and I, no way. I cannot. I do not want to be dictated to by man. We live in a postmodern world now. Back then, marriage was a tool or gateway to attain wealth; look at lobola for African peoples and dowry in Mediaeval Europe.

Sharon: No, you got it wrong, ilobola is for building ties between families and showing gratitude to the bride's family.

Nicole: But there is cyclical wealth creation that flows and revolves around that. Marriage may be good but for me, I can't shame. Men expect us to be subservient and nurse them like babies. That is something I cannot do.

Sharon: I find it hard to comprehend. You are the elder sister. I should look up at you. *(She is dishing out.)*

Nicole: You see. *(Pointing her hand to her.)* Back in the day, the firstborn daughter had to be a model for her younger sisters. Just look at that trash of Katherine's saga in the Taming of the Shrew. Katherine challenged patriarchal hetero-normative paradigms, moreover was psychologically and even physically abused to submit to patriarchy. Starving someone is physical abuse.

Sharon: I cannot believe you compare Elizabethan England norms with 21st-century men, in particular a man like Valentine.

Nicole*: (She laughs).* There might be a sliver of truth that society has transgressed so much since 1950, let alone the 16th-century Elizabethan England. Nevertheless; some things never change. Let's eat dear, I'll make the dessert.

Sharon: Cool. How are things between you and Luke?

Nicole: O please don't ask me about that one, I'm through with him.

Sharon: *(acclaimed.)* What! What happened?

Nicole: I can't stand to be ghosted for weeks, even a month, whereby a person deliberately ignores your texts and calls. Blue ticking is the worst thing ever in a relationship. Then he comes up with endless excuses.

Sharon: I'm so sorry, he seems so nice though.

Nicole: Exactly, he's so excellent in portraying himself as the sweetest, open and talkative person. Moreover, what he does to me-it has aggrieved my heart. Dating a cold person, shall afflict you to the core-that's Luke.

Sharon: I'm sorry dear. *(Reaching out her hand.)* You shall find someone better, that shall complement you to the fullest.

Exeunt

7.1.8 Scene Eight

(The following week, Fish Hoek, a family home, enter Precious and Cynthia, in the lounge, watching a Flat Screen Digital Television.)

Cynthia: You are so focused on your cell phone, it's like I am not even present, Precious.

Precious: Hmm...What?

Cynthia: What are you busy with? Are you on that Mix-It of yours?

Precious: You wouldn't understand. I just can't comprehend why you cannot see how funny and enjoyable it is.

Cynthia: What's funny and enjoyable about it? The sexual topics you engage in there, for there is not something productive and upbringing about it.

Precious: There is some sliver of truth in what you are saying, but it is more than that. You do get deep meaningful conversations with people who are strangers; who sound so informed, opinionated, empathetic and understanding than all the people you know.

Cynthia: With pseudonyms? I can never comprehend people's addiction on Mix-It.

Precious: Remember I met Casanova on Mix it? Look at how things are folding up now.

Cynthia: At least it is someone we know, which brings me to the question; how are things between you and him?

Precious: I do not know; I do not know; I am not sure even what decision can I take; remember Bachelor is interested in me as well. Even though thought he hasn't said anything, but I can see, and people talk.

Cynthia: Really? So you are not sure which one to choose?

Precious: Yes.

Cynthia: O please, you can't date Bachelor, remember I am dating his friend: then you and I are sisters, there would be no peace with that; besides, I am uncertain of Bachelor's experiment with love.

Precious: That's cold... you do not need an experience for this, it comes out naturally.

Cynthia: Let's say then that you date him; how shall that work? These guys shall come simultaneously to check on us. Talk about how they made love with each of us. That shall devalue ourselves. I wouldn't say take Casanova, for he is fuck boy, a chameleon... as I have noticed how he is suddenly fond of me to be sympathetic to him, now that he wants you.

Precious: So, what would you advise me to do, then?

Cynthia: The decision shall be yours in the end. I don't want you to say I decided for you that you would later regret.

Precious: But you have already done that by giving Bachelor a red flag.

Cynthia: That is because of how it shall affect my relationship with Charles. Just think about yourself, give it your cognizance. At the end of the day, these two guys are not the only dudes in Cape Town. There is plenty of fish in the sea.

Precious: Okay, only time shall tell.

Exeunt

7.1.9 Scene Nine

(In a week, Fish Hoek, a street, 10th Avenue Road; enter Bachelor, he walking, while busy texting via Facebook.)

Bachelor: Where are you?

    Precious: At school.

    Bachelor: Can I see you?

    Precious: Why?

    Bachelor: *(Thinking, having an intra-conversation).* What am I going to say? I do not want to offend her. If she responds badly and mocks me? *(He responds).* Never mind, I mean... I hope you are well.

    Precious*: (text)* Yes, I am. What were you going to say?

    Bachelor: (text) I was just checking up on you to see if you are fine.

    Precious: *(text).* How are you?

    Bachelor*: (Text).* I am well.

    Precious: *(Text)* Cool. Bye.

    Bachelor*: (nervous).* What did I say? I may have turned her off. I just find it difficult to be firm and bold, to express myself; but then, it has always been like this since I was at crèche; I have been mocked and ridiculed a lot. Some childhood trauma may be catching up with me. I need to change, just as seasons do; when vegetation withers in autumn as in now, die in winter and regrow in spring in September to bring soothing blooms in summer by December. People must see some good attracting qualities in me. I cannot endure remaining in this despair.

    Enter Charles

    Charles: You seem to be in so many deep thoughts, let me see. *(He grabs the cell phone.)*

Bachelor: *(Trying to grab it back.)* No Charles, you are going to break my touch screen. No, do not read. *(Charles reads his conversation.)*

Charles: No way, this is not how you text someone you crush on, otherwise, you are going to get crushed. Let me help you. *(He texts).*

Bachelor: No Charles.

Charles: Relax, just chill. *(He writes the texts).* Sorry about earlier. I was busy with something. Precious, you are one of the sweetest and gentlest girls I know. I have longed to express how I feel about you. I admire and adore your lovely and livelier personality; I would be glad if I would go on a date with you. I cannot help myself with your irresistible countenance. You are so overwhelmingly beautiful and adorable.

(Sent.)

Bachelor: Let me see. *(He reads the text.)* Charles, what did you do? What if she rages and storms at me?

Charles: No, she won't trust me on this one. What brings you here?

Bachelor: To see some of our intermediaries. Thereafter, I went to see my uncle.

Charles: Cool, are you enjoying what are busy with?

Bachelor: Yes of course, I want to have proficient aptitudes; which is why I took some gap year-assist Valentine with the running of the company; I have always been involved since young age, but was busy with school. How is college?

Charles: False Bay College, is spot on!

Bachelor: That's great, I wish you the best. Let's grab something to eat at spur nearby.

Charles: Budget...

Bachelor: *(Laughs.)* Since when do I need to budget to out my friend?

Charles :(*Low smile.*) Cool.

Bachelor: Come, I have parked my car nearby.

Exeunt.

7.1.10 Scene Ten

(Hout Bay, a room in Helen's Hotel, enters Casanova, he is chatting with Precious on Mix-IT, and Casanova is laying on his bed.)

Casanova: Hey beautiful! How are you?

Precious: Hey! I am well, thanks. How about you?

Casanova: I am doing well, thanks. I was just thinking, we've been talking for a while now and I enjoy our conversations. I wondering if you would go on a date with me sometime?

Precious: Oh, umm... that's sweet of you to ask, Casanova; but I am not sure if I am interested in dating anyone right now.

Casanova: Oh, I understand. But just hear me out. I promise I am not like other guys. I genuinely enjoy spending time with you and I think we could have a great time together. Plus, I am not looking at anything serious right now. We could just have some fun and see where things go.

Precious: I appreciate your honesty, but I just do not want to get involved with someone who might not be interested in looking for the same things as me.

Casanova: I get where you are coming from, but I promise you shall not regret going out with me. I shall make it worth your while.

Precious: Ha-ha... you are quite a charmer, aren't you?

Casanova: *(Laughs.)* I have been told that before. So what do you say? Shall you go on a date with me?

Precious: Alright, you've convinced me. Let's do it.

Casanova: Yes! That is what I like to hear. How about we go out this weekend? I know a great sushi place somewhere in Hout Bay.

Precious: Sounds good to me, I'll hear from you.

Casanova: Perfect. I can't wait to see you. *(Precious logs out.)* Yes! *(Shaking his head, and hitting the bed with his feet).*

(Rose Enters, she is coming from the bathroom, wearing a gown)

Rose: I wonder what are you gladdened about.

Casanova: It's nothing, baby. Come here. *(Rose sits on the bed and gives him her hand.)*

Casanova: You are so lovely. *(Kissing her hand.)*

Rose: Stop being naughty. I am leaving now. I do not want your girlfriend to catch me here.

Casanova: No, she will not.

Rose: How do I know? I am not even certain who your actual girlfriend is since you are such a womaniser. I hate myself for deliberately getting into this love circle of yours, willingly and knowingly, that you are a player. *(He wakes up, kneels on the bed and holds her from the back and kisses her).*

Rose: *(excited.)* Casanova! No... *(Laughing.)*

Casanova: I love the way you are the only one who gets it, Rose. Your company is astoundingly pleasurable.

Rose: Hmmm, you are so romantic and sweet, Casanova. *(They kiss.)*

Exeunt.

7.1.11 Scene Eleven

(Valentine and Sharon are walking hand in hand through the local botanical gardens: the Kirstenbosch botanical garden nestled at the eastern foot of Table Mountain in Cape Town. It's a beautiful autumn evening. The air is crisp and the leaves are turning shades of red, orange, and gold. They stroll along the winding paths, enjoying the colours and fragrances of the fresh flowers and plants.)

Valentine: Sharon, do you remember when we first came here on New Year's Day in 2000?

Sharon: *(smiling.)* Of course, I do. It feels like a lifetime ago.

Valentine: It does, doesn't it? We've been through so much together since then.

Sharon: *(nodding.)* And we've always made it through.

Valentine: That's right. We've had some tough times, but we've always been there for each other. And through it all, I've realized that I never want to spend a day without you by my side.

Sharon: *(gazing into his eyes.)* Valentine, I feel the same way. You are my rock, my best friend, my soul mate.

Valentine: *(squeezing her hands.)* Sharon, I love you more than anything in this world. You've been there for me through thick and thin, and I want to spend eternity with you.

Sharon: *(tearfully.)* Oh, Valentine, I love you too. I want to spend eternity with you, too.

Valentine: *(getting down on one knee and pulling out a ring box.)* Sharon, will you do me the honour of becoming my wife?

Sharon: *(gasping.)* Yes, yes, a thousand times yes!

Valentine: (slipping the ring on her finger) I'm so happy, Sharon. You've made me the happiest man in the world.

Sharon: *(kissing him.)* And you've made me the happiest woman. I can't wait to spend forever with you.

Valentine: Me too. I can't wait for Easter; we should go, celebrate and commemorate Christ's death and resurrection. Praise him for being the Lord forever and ever, for keeping us alive and enduring our relationship, despite the hindrances we have been through.

Sharon: Absolutely. Good Friday is on the 2nd of April, right?

Valentine: Yes. It's also a day 10 holiday, as schools have closed.

Exeunt

7.1.12 Scene Twelve

(As Precious gets ready for her date with Casanova, she carefully selects her outfit for the chilly autumn evening in Hout Bay, Cape Town.
She chooses a knee-length, dark green wrap dress made of soft, cosy fabric that's perfect for the cool weather. The dress is fitted at the waist and flares out slightly, giving her a feminine and flattering silhouette.
She pairs the dress with a stylish wide-brimmed hat made of soft, black felt that matches her dress perfectly. The hat is adorned with a simple but elegant black ribbon that ties at the back, adding a touch of sophistication to her look.
To complete her outfit, Precious chooses a pair of ankle-high black leather boots with a small heel. The boots are both comfortable and fashionable, perfect for walking around the city and keeping her feet warm on the chilly autumn evening.
As she stands in front of the mirror, she adjusts her hat and smooth out her dress, feeling confident and beautiful. She can't wait to see Casanova and spend the evening with him, enjoying the crisp autumn air and the beauty of the city.)

Precious: I could not be more beautiful than this; it is the 10th of April; a generally mild and pleasant weather with comfortable temperatures and lower humidity. This dress fits perfectly, I couldn't be more thrilled. I am so excited to meet him on our date, I have not been in Hout Bay for a long-time, last I was there was on New Year's Day.

Cynthia Enters

Cynthia: *(Shocked, and smiling).* And then... *(Bewildered),* where are you going?

Precious: Nowhere. *(Brushing herself, she comes towards the door unto her).* I am just going out, taking myself out.

Cynthia: O please, little sister...I am old enough to see when a woman is dressed up for a man

Cynthia: *(cheerful and grinning.)* Who is he? *(She tries to grab her, the precious steps back)*

69

Precious: Okay... You do not have to be violent. It's him...

Cynthia: Who? *(Bewildered, animated and sparkling.)* Do not tell me it's Casanova?

Precious: He asked me for sushi date in Hout Bay.

Cynthia: That guy, is so romantic but he is such an ass...

Precious: Are you disgruntled?

Cynthia: No, I just wonder what conniving words he used on you to make you go on with him.

Precious: Cynthia please...

(Down casted.): do not ruin my mood, just allow me to make my own mistakes, do you remember how Robert used you, you were so dishearten, you even lost weight until Charles found you.

Cynthia: Yhooo, did have to bring all that up?

(Disgruntled): Well, all I can say is: good luck. Have a best evening. Let me fix you here at the back.

Precious: What?

Cynthia: Your hair, it's not tightened well.

(Precious turns around and faces the bed, she fixes, and then they go to the mirror.)

Cynthia: You look stunning, I am so impressed by your dress code that compliments cooler temperatures in the early morning and evening, the wind that blows from light breezes too strong gusts.

Precious: Thank you. Let me check the time, grab my cell phone for me, please. *(Cynthia, gives her.)*

Cynthia: Is he going to fetch you here?

Precious: I shall meet him at the hexagon centre, by Fish Hoek Traffic Services.

(She checks Facebook inbox and sees Bachelor's text.)

Precious: (surprised) O my...I am just seeing this now, from Bachelor.

Cynthia: Let me see... *(She raises her hand and arm to reach Precious[1].)*

Precious: He sent it like a week ago, around the same time Casanova asked me out, I didn't see the text.

Cynthia: *(Takes the cell phone and reads.)* Wow, I am impressed, he sent this. I cannot believe it too; it can't be him

Precious: What do you mean it cannot be him? Is that not his account?

Cynthia: *(takes a deep breath.)* I am just astounded. What are you going to do now?

Precious: Nothing has changed, I am going, and then I shall take from there?

Cynthia: Are you planning to go on a date with both them?

Precious: *(weary.)* I do not know, time shall tell.

(She sighs.): Do not ruin my mood asking about that. *(Subdues).* Now how do I look? *(She turns around and round.)*

Cynthia: Perfect. Whatever happens from now on, but please, remember what we spoke about weeks back. *(She stands up).* You look stunning my sister, I wish all the best, though I do not like that boy but, people change, maybe his teenage swings are so up.

Precious: Cynthia, can you please stop with all this negativity. Let me. Go. *(She takes a purse).*

Cynthia: Hug, please. Let's take a selfie. *(They embrace and take a picture.)* I love you so dearly.

Precious: Thank you. I love you too.

Exeunt

7.1.13 Scene Thirteen

(Hout Bay, a harbour town in the City of Cape Town, Western Cape[1] province of South Africa[2]; situated in a valley on the Atlantic seaboard of the Cape Peninsula[3], twenty kilometres south of Cape Town[4] CBD.
Enter Casanova and Precious, a restaurant by the harbour: Casanova is wearing a long-sleeved, collared shirt in a solid navy colour, the collar adds a touch of formality and long sleeves providing warmth; a pair of black jeans, creating a clean, streamlined countenance; a lightweight indigo jacket complementing his shirt and black leather shoes, comfortable for walking on the beach along the coast.)

Casanova: *(Anticipation.)* This is a great spot. I love the view of the harbour and the beach from here. Hout Bay's local colour and scenery make it a tourist attraction among both local and international visitors. I am drawn by the variety of restaurants here.

Precious: Yeah, and it's only a few steps away from the luxurious accommodations along the coast. It's the perfect location for a date.

(Joyful): I love its geographical position for scenery, hiking and mount climbing; the surrounding by mountains to the north, east and west and the southern Atlantic Ocean to the south.

Casanova: *(Appeased.)* Don't forget the northern bordering by the Table Mountain National Park[5] comprising the Orangekloof Nature reserve and the bottom slopes of Table Mountain beyond that; its north-west bordered by the backside of the Twelve Apostles.

Precious: *(In agreement and excitement.)* Exactly; its beauty is astounding and captivating: when you gaze upon the western side,

---

1. *https://en.wikipedia.org/wiki/Western_Cape*

2. *https://en.wikipedia.org/wiki/South_Africa*

3. *https://en.wikipedia.org/wiki/Cape_Peninsula*

4. *https://en.wikipedia.org/wiki/Cape_Town*

5. https://en.wikipedia.org/wiki/Table_Mountain_National_Park

bordered by Little Lion's Head, Karbonkelberg[6], Kaptein's Peak and the Sentinel[7]; you are mesmerised; then take your eye to the eastern side, bordered by the Vlakkenberg, Skoorsteenskopberg and Constantiaberg, it blows your mind.

Casanova: Definitely...then there is that Chapman's Peak drive carved out of the mountainside and leads towards Noordhek and onwards to the Cape Point.

Precious: (Excitement.) I just adore the variety and order of the architectural style here.

Casanova: And the Victorian architecture of this restaurant is so unique. I love how they've incorporated it into the interior design.

Precious: It's beautiful. The chandeliers and the ornate details on the walls are so elegant, and the high ceilings and large windows make it feel spacious and airy.

Casanova: *(Relaxation.)* Agreed; and with the weather cooling down in autumn, it's nice to have a cosy restaurant to come to for our sushi date.

Precious: I'm so excited for the sushi. I've heard this place has the best in town.

Casanova: Yeah, I heard they use fresh, locally sourced ingredients, and their sushi is prepared by master chefs.

[The waiter approaches the table to take their order.]

Waiter: Good evening. Can I start you off with some drinks?

Precious: Yes, please. I'll have a hot green tea.

Casanova: And I'll have a sake.

Waiter: Excellent choices. Are you ready to order some sushi?

Precious: Definitely. I'll have the California roll and the spicy tuna roll.

Casanova: And I'll have the rainbow roll and the dragon roll.

Waiter: Great choices. Your sushi will be out shortly.

---

6.   https://en.wikipedia.org/wiki/Karbonkelberg

7.   https://en.wikipedia.org/wiki/The_Sentinel,_Hout_Bay

Precious: Thank you. I can't wait to taste it.

Casanova: Me too. This is such a beautiful restaurant, and the location couldn't be better. I'm glad we chose this place for our autumn sushi date. *(The Waiter goes.)*

Precious: Me too. It's the perfect way to enjoy the beautiful views and the delicious sushi while staying cosy and warm. *(A moment of pause.)*

Precious*: (Curious)* You seem to love this place so much?

Casanova: Absolutely, but also; my mother owns some hotel and accommodation here. I would be glad to own mine someday, this place booms with tourist all over the country and abroad, and they come book these resorts. It does parallel Fish Hoek, it just more luxurious with many 5-star hotels. *(The waiter brings the starters)*

Precious: It... *(A moment of pause, they are both looking at the waiter)*.

Waiter: Here are your starters... *(Puts them on the table.)*

Both: Thank you.

Waiter: Anything else?

Precious: Lemonade please.

Casanova: Me too please!

Waiter: Coming right up *(the waiter goes.)*

Precious: What was I saying? Hmm...Yes... I was saying it is such an economically thriving place, its fishing industry, finance and accommodation are spot on.

(She pauses for a moment)

Precious: *(Embarrassed)* It's pity I have not slept in these resorts.

Casanova: *(Laughing)* Do not worry, I'll take you there sometime.

Precious: Hahahahahahah. *(Grinning)*. You are naughty. *(Sipping a juice)*

Casanova: *(Laughing.)* Your mind is so fast, I hadn't even mentioned anything. Moreover, I know a place you might like; the

Flora Bay Resort. It is at the base of the scenic Chapman's Peak Drive; it's a casual beachfront resort overlooking the Atlantic Ocean and five kilometres away from the World of Birds Wildlife Sanctuary and Monkey Park, and 14 km from Kirstenbosch National Botanical Garden.

Precious: I'd be glad, I have heard about it and seen it from afar. *(The waiter brings their Suhsi and Lemonades.)*

Both: Thank You

Casanova: I am so glad you came, you are so beautiful, and your outfit is in flame.

Precious: You are not so bad, you as well... *(Laughing).* You are so elegant.

Casanova: Thank so much. *(They eat).* When I firstly asked you, I was so panic stricken.

Precious: *(smiling.)* You are such a liar; you, of all people...

Casanova: I am serious. *(Elated.)* I have always seen you at Fish Hoke High School, but was so reserved and nervous to ask you out, we've spoken only at time when their other people.

Precious: *(Smitten.)* Well... now you found me...

Casanova: *(Contentment.)* I am so thrilled, we seem to have such magnet and flowing.

Precious: *(Laughing, leaning back to her chair and then sits straight.)* Precious: *(enthusiastic.)* You are such a charmer, are you?

Casanova: *I guess so. (Affectionate.) I* feel so at eased when I am with you. So complete.

Precious: I just adore you; you are so pleasing. *(Pleased.)*

Casanova: You and I, I feel like we shall go into places.

Precious: (Eagerness.) What places?

Casanova: Adventures of fulfilment and delight.

Precious: *(Takes a deep breath.)* Only time shall tell, nevertheless, I could not be anywhere else than here today the 2nd of April 2010. *(Charmed.)*

Casanova: I am impressed and charmed. You like green?

Precious: Yes, green is my favourite colour, in particular olive green. And you?

Casanova: I love dark colours like dark blue, indigo and navy; they give you that alleviation.

Precious: Since you said you dream to won your own hotel and holiday resort someday, what are your aspirations as of now?

Casanova: I have thought doing Bachelor of Business Science, or anything related to hotel management and tourism. There is a lot of money in this industry, and businesses are going to make a lot of money in this 2010 FIFA world cup; and also, it seems South Africa joining the BRIC bloc soon than later to make BRICS; the powerful grouping of the world's leading emerging market economies, namely Brazil, Russia, India, China and South Africa. The BRICS mechanism aims to promote peace, security, development and cooperation. So, we may see a lot of tourist and immigration from Latin America, Eastern Europe and Far East; as compared to the past when it has been dominated by the Global North.

Precious: *(Fascinated.)* Wow, I am so impressed.

Casanova: What is your interest?

Precious: Well...looking at the trends, it seems this decade shall be driven by significant advancements in digital technologies, particularly in the areas of mobile devices, social media, cloud computing, and artificial intelligence. The widespread adoption of smartphones and tablets, along with the availability of high-speed internet, led to the proliferation of digital services and the emergence of the sharing economy. I am keen on computer science, software engineering and robotics. I'm fascinated by What's App; it's pity my mobile cell phone E250 isn't engineered for it.

Casanova: which mobile cell phone do?

Precious: Apple iPhone like yours.

Casanova: Impressive, I had thought it's available for other smartphones, as long as they have internet.

Precious: No, cell phones like Samsung E250 and Nokia Xpress Music are not capable of running WhatsApp as they do not meet the minimum requirements for running the app. WhatsApp requires a smartphone running on Android 4.0.3 or later, iOS 9.0 or later, or certain versions of KaiOS. Those two runs on their respective proprietary operating systems and do not support WhatsApp. They can run Facebook and Twitter on limited capacity, as functionality compared to emerging smartphones. The Nokia Xpress Music has a built-in Facebook and Twitter app, but the app's functionality may be limited compared to the full-featured versions available on latest trending smartphones like Apple iPhone. A Samsung E250 does not have a built-in Facebook or Twitter app, but it may be possible to access these services through the phone's internet browser. However, due to the limited capabilities of these older phones, the experience of using Facebook and Twitter on them may are not as smooth or seamless as latest ones.

Casanova: *(impressed.)* Wow, you're so smart. Let's make a toast. *(They take cheers.)*

Casanova: I desire and pray for all our visions and mission be fulfilled.

Precious: In Jesus Christ Name.

Casanova: Amen.

Precious: I'm feeling adventurous.

Casanova: I love that about you. You're always up for anything.

Precious: I feel like I can be myself around you. You make me feel so comfortable."

Casanova: That's because I really like you. I want you to be yourself around me always.

Precious: I like you too. I feel like we have a really great connection, and I'm excited to see where this goes.

Casanova: Me too. I have a feeling that we're going to have a lot of fun together.

(*They smile at each other, and the chemistry between them is palpable.*)

Exeunt

7.1.14 Scene Fourteen

(Enter Sharon and Nicole, a family home, Fish Hoek, in a sitting room.)

S **haron:** *(Elated and singing)*. Life is so nice.

Nicole: I wonder what you are so thrilled about.

Sharon: Nicole, I have trying to resonate with about something; you know as sisters, we have a duty to our family and to the society: and that duty includes getting married and starting a family.

Nicole: *(Smiling)* I am already aware of your desires and what shall you say, moreover; as for me, I do not want to get married, I cannot imagine myself being tied to one person for the rest of my life.

Sharon: *(Astonished)*. What do you mean you not will to get married? You know, we have to give our mother some grandchildren, you do not want a lonely miserable life in your old age, and in our family who hasn't got married, just look at Cindy, our cousin got married at 27 years. What the family wills the most, is for us to have stable partners and fulfilment. Let alone at church.

Nicole: *(Firmly.)* I understand that, Sharon; but society has transgressed and revalorised so much, we are not living in Victorian England of stringent societal norms. People have now realised they can choose their own path in life, have their own accord regarding marriage. I have decided that marriage isn't for me. I am quite astounded and perplexed for someone who is an advocate like you believe on that. You always see in courts, how these things end up.

Sharon: I get your point, and I have thought thoroughly, I do not want to be cold and lonely in my old age, but also; will to have a partner I shall enjoy my youth and middle age with. Most importantly, think about your own family, and what father would have wanted. He would be thrilled to walk his two daughters down the aisle.

Nicole: *(Calmly.)* I get your concern. But I do not think our family's reputation should dictate my choices, I need to adventure and fulfil my own happiness in my own accord, even going against societal norms.

Sharon: *(Laughing.)* Don't you desire to have children?

Nicole: *(Smiling.)* I do not need to get married to have children, I can have them out of wedlock; as they used to say, there is variety of ways of having children like adopting. Also, this world is so evil, I do not want to bring innocent souls to this mess. I am contempt in living on my own.

Sharon: You are so secularised...*(pausing.)* but I get your point Nicole, though it is different from mine. I always thought marriage and children are the most important things in life.

Nicole: *(Nodding.)* And that is fine, we do not have to be in agreement all the time, as long as we are going to be civil with one another; if we were always in agreement as a species, we would still be living in stone age.

Sharon: I understand, Nicole, I want you have the most fulfilling life, even if you are not getting married.

Nicole :(*Smiling.)* Thank you, Sharon, appreciate your support, maybe I may change my mind someday, moreover; as of now, I am happy living life in my own accord.

Sharon: How about now? (Showing her a left hand of hers with a ring, with delightful eyes)

Nicole: *(Elated and standing, running to embrace her.)* what! Why did you not say all this time? I am over the moon my dear sister. Finally, you are going to be Mrs Green.

Sharon: Thank you.

Nicole: Tell me, I want to hear every detail, even the slightest. When did he propose, and where?

Sharon*: At the Kirstenbosch botanical garden[1], with winds blowing withering orange yellowish leaves.

Nicole*: *(Enthusiastic.)* Tell me more, tell me more.

Exeunt

---

1.   https://en.wikipedia.org/wiki/Botanical_garden

7.2 Act Two
7.2.1 Scene One

(On Saturday, at noon; Bachelor wandering around the town square, lost in thought. Fish Hoek has a beach of about 1.5 kilometres and is quite flat; with the bay protected from the currents and stronger surf in the rest of False Bay. Swimming is permitted along the entire beach, and lifeguards are on duty; body surfing, boogie boarding, windsurfing, and kayaking are popular activities.
He had just finished talking to his friend Charles about his crush on Charles' girlfriend's sister, Precious, and was feeling hopeful that she would go on a date with him after he had asked her out. As he turned a corner, he suddenly collided with a girl who was walking in the opposite direction.
Bachelor exclaimed, almost falling backwards. He quickly regained his balance and looked up to see a girl staring at him, looking annoyed.)

Bachelor: *(Smiling.)* Cynthia, I haven't seen you in a while. I almost could not recognise you; how are you?

Cynthia: *(weak smile.)* I am well; thank you.

Bachelor: Where is Precious?

Cynthia: *(Frowning.)* She's at home. What are you going to do?

Bachelor: *(Disappointed.)* That's so cold, I was just asking...

Cynthia: *(Aggressive.)* You think I do not know what you are trying to do? But please do not.

Bachelor: What are you talking about?

Cynthia: I am talking about you asking Precious on a date.

(Angrily.) Seriously? Do you not understand that I'm dating Charles, your friend? You are a good man, Bachelor, but you cannot be with my sister. Just think about it yourself.

Bachelor: *(defensively.)* Look, I didn't know it was that big of a deal. Precious and I just hit it off when we spoke sometime back.

Cynthia: *(frustrated.)* Of course, it's a big deal! Precious is my sister, and I don't want her dating my boyfriend's friend? It's too complicated. I do not know what you are trying to accomplish, but it cannot work; there are plenty of fish in the sea, and you shall find a lady that shall compliment you, for Precious isn't the one.

Bachelor: *(sighing.)* I understand your concern, but can't you just let Precious and I make our own decisions? We're not doing anything wrong. You seem to have a strong opinion about who she should date.

Cynthia: *(angrily.)* You're not getting it, are you? It's not just about you and Precious. It's about how this will affect all of us. I don't want to deal with the drama that will come from this. It's not because I dislike or hate you; I just want nothing that will ruin my relationship with Charles. Just imagine, we are sisters, and we are dating friends? It is almost the same as two sisters dating brothers. It's unethical, and it does not sound right.

Bachelor: *(apologetically.)* I'm sorry, Cynthia. I didn't mean to cause any problems between us. I just thought that Precious was really cool and wanted to get to know her better.

Cynthia: *(calming down.)* I know you didn't mean it. But please, can you just hold off on pursuing anything with Precious for now? It's just not a good idea.

Bachelor: *(nodding.)* Okay, I'll back off. It'll be difficult though, and I don't want to aggravate things between us.

Cynthia: *(smiling.)* Thank you. Just try, I would really appreciate it.

Bachelor: *(smiling back.)* No problem. I value our friendship and want nothing to ruin it.

Cynthia: (Grinning.) Pleasure... *(she takes steps, and stops.)* And by the way, I am glad you can see this, for Precious recently went on a date with Casanova.

Bachelor: *(shocked.)* What? You then allowed that?

Cynthia: Who am I to decide for her? It's not like I said, "Absolutely, you can go". I know who that guy is.

Bachelor: *(harshly.)* But Cynthia!

Cynthia: Dude, I do not want to get into any kind of feud between you two. I do not understand why you are at each other's throats like cats. You even have such a resemblance, which I cannot understand.

Bachelor: I am tired of people saying I resemble Casanova in countenance.

Cynthia: *(Calm.)* Okay, fine. I will see you.

Exit.

Bachelor: What in the world is this? *(As Bachelor walked alone in the quiet street, his mind was racing with a jumble of conflicting emotions; as he had just received the news that Precious, the girl he had been longing for, had gone on a date with his enemy, Casanova. It felt like a dagger through his heart.*

He had just come to terms with the fact that he couldn't pursue Precious, thanks to his conversation with Cynthia. But now, the news of her date with Casanova made him feel like he had lost something he had never even had. He goes and gets in a midnight black Mercedes-Benz C-Class 2010-2011, sits down, and puts his hands on the steering).

Bachelor: *(frustrated and inflicted.)* Once again, he has grabbed what I want like an eagle catching a hen's chick. I am so pissed!

Exit.

7.2.2 Scene Two

(Fish Hoek High School, 13th Ave., Fish Hoek, Cape Town: a hexagon and rectangular paths surround it; around their school there are clinics, businesses, suburban houses, law firms, accounting firms, and a hospital: it is in the morning, just before the first classes, in a grade 12 classroom; enter Precious and Ruth.)

Ruth: *(curious.)* Hey, Precious, I heard you went on a date with Casanova last weekend. How was it? And why him?

Precious: *(aroused and thrilled.)* He is just so great and so romantic; we had such flowing conversation and deep chemistry.

Ruth: Where did you have it?

Precious: We went to Hout Bay. He fetched me here with the latest 2010 Ford Ranger 2.2 DHP XL Cab; thereafter, we drove to Hout Bay. It was so amazing.

Ruth: Hmmm *(enthusiastic.)* I want the juicy part.

Precious: We went to this amazing restaurant; the food was beyond tasteful and mouth-watering.

Ruth: *(Amazed.)* It sounds like fun! What did you wear?

Precious: *(Elated.)* I wore a knee-length, dark green wrap dress made of soft, cosy fabric that's perfect for the cool weather. The dress fitted at my waist and flared out slightly, giving me a feminine and flattering silhouette. Then I paired it with a stylish wide-brimmed hat made of soft black felt; the outfit was astounding, with the hat adorned with an elegant black ribbon. Then I put on a pair of ankle-high black leather boots with a small heel.

Ruth: *(amused.)* It sounds so chic! I can't wait to see the photos. How was Casanova?

Precious: He was superb, and appealingly appetising, with his irresistible countenance. He wore a long-sleeved, collared shirt in a solid navy colour, the collar added a touch of formality and long sleeves provided warmth; a pair of black jeans, creating a clean, streamlined countenance; then he put on a lightweight indigo jacket complementing his shirt and black leather shoes, comfortable for walking on the beach along the coast.

Ruth: *(fascinated.)* Wow, I can only dream... to go on date with a guy like him.

Precious: Look, we wanted to wear something that compliments the autumn season (showing her photos). He bought me a cluster of grapes and guava juice when he finished.

(In the same scenery, two mitres away; a dialogue between two leaners.)

Learner 1: Did you hear that Precious went on a date with Casanova?

Learner 2: Ugh, I can't believe she went on a date with him. He is such a player and has dated like half if not two-thirds of girls in school.

Learner 3: What! *(Shocked and amused, coming from the side.)* The one and only Casanova who matriculated last year with Bachelor, Cynthia, Charles, Ntombi, and the rest?

Learner 1: Exactly. *(Irritated.)* The one and only!

Learner 3: *(Amazed.)* I don't get why she would give him the time of day.

Learner 2: I heard he is just using her to add another girl to the list. He uses his irresistible countenance, and his parent's luxurious cars to lure girls.

Learner 1: His mother is so rich; she owns some 5-star hotel in Hout Bay.

Learner 2: She should know better than to fall for his tricks.

Learner 3: I hope she realises soon what kind of guy he is before she gets hurt. That's not even his real parent. I once heard he was adopted.

Learner 1 and Learner 2: What! (*Shocked.*)

(*Suddenly, Mr. Andrews enters; the leaners stand up and greet him; they sit down.*)

Exeunt

7.2.3 Scene Three

(At Green Point, at noon, in an office, enter Bachelor and Valentine.)

Valentine: Hey, Bachelor, can we talk for a minute?

Bachelor: Sure, what's up?

Valentine: Well, I have some big news. I proposed to Sharon last night, and she said yes!

Bachelor: *(Thrilled and amused.)* Wow, that's amazing! Congratulations! I'm so happy for you. When is the big day?

Valentine: *(Happy.)* We haven't set a date yet. We want to take our time and enjoy the engagement for a bit; we'll definitely let you know as soon as we plan.

Bachelor: (Elated.) I cannot wait, dear brother; I'm looking forward to it. Sharon is great, and I think she'll be a wonderful addition to our family.

Valentine: *(Sadden.)* I'm glad you think so. Speaking of family, I've been thinking a lot about our parents lately. I cannot forget that day.

Bachelor: (Grieves.) It's hard to believe, and it is even harder for me since I do not even know what they looked like, and only in pictures do I know them.

Valentine: *(saddened.)* I know. But I'm grateful that we have each other and that we've been able to carry on their legacy with the wine company and our mother's hotel there in Hout Bay.

Bachelor: *(Awakened.)* Absolutely. Our uncle did a great job of taking care of us, but now it's up to us to make sure the business thrives. The hotel is another story, since it is in someone else's hands.

Valentine: *(Zealous.)* I agree, and with Sharon by my side, having done law and now being an advocate, I feel like we can accomplish anything. I'm just so happy to have her in my life; she is so intelligent and a family person, which is why I proposed to her.

Bachelor: *(fascinated.)* I can tell. You're practically glowing! I'm happy for you, Val. You deserve all the happiness in the world.

Valentine: *(Appeased.)* Thanks, Bachelor. That means a lot coming from you. I'm excited to start this new chapter in my life and to continue building our family legacy with you by my side. Speaking of family business, I have been thinking about what the future holds for you. I am glad that you are shadowing me and taking a gap year before deciding what to do for your career.

Bachelor: That's amazing, Val! Thank you so much. I have been learning a lot from you and can't wait to become a part of the family business.

Valentine: *(enthusiastic.)* I'm excited to have you on board, Bachelor. And since you're finishing your gap year by summer, I thought you could start studying a bachelor's in business science or anything related next year. What do you think?

Bachelor*: (elated and amazed.)* That's exactly what I was planning to do! You must be reading my mind. I'm so glad that we're on the same page.

Valentine: I always knew we were a great team. And now, with Sharon in the picture, our family is even stronger.

Bachelor: I couldn't agree more. I'm so glad we have each other, Val. We've been through so much together, and I know we'll always be there for each other, no matter what.

Valentine: That's right, Bachelor. We're family, and nothing can change that.

Bachelor: I am so glad. I love you, brother. *(They embrace.)*

Valentine: I love you too.

Exeunt

7.2.4 Scene Four

(A coffee shop; enter Andrews and Marry.)

Andrews: We need to be careful now; otherwise, we are going to get caught. People are getting suspicious now, given the way we get so cosy, even at school.

Marry: Yea, I think we should refrain from being cosy at school; we wouldn't want to ruin our reputation and career for a mere sexual gratification.

Andrews: (Smiling.) The problem is, I cannot resist you; you have that magnet. You are so astoundingly beautiful.

Marry: You are flirting with me now. *(Laughing.)* You can't help yourself.

Andrews: I can't, dear. They touch each other's hands and get cosy. I just enjoy your company. I love you.

Marry: *(Enthralled).* Please do not play with me. (They kiss). (At a distance, Precious is sitting with Casanova.)

Precious: Look over there. *(Astonished.)* Isn't that, Mr. Andrews?

Casanova: Yes, that's him.

Precious: My goodness, he is cheating on his wife?

Casanova: They have been doing this for quite some time. I once spotted them.

Precious: *(She takes a picture of them from afar.)*

Casanova: No! Why did you do that?

Precious: I cannot believe this. Poor Charles! The gentlest guy with high morale, I know.

Casanova: It seems like his trustworthiness, genuineness, and pacifist instincts were not inherited from his father.

Precious: It's a shame he would be devastated by this-he's such an upright young man with integrity. Please, he cannot know this. He cannot find out about this.

Casanova: Then why did you take the picture?

Precious: You know Andrews is so strict with marks when marking a paper? I am thinking of having something to hold on to for him in case I fail.

Casanova: So, you are going to blackmail him? You know that's illegal right? *(laughing)*

(Mary and Andrews suddenly recognise that there are Casanova and Precious in this arena; they quickly pack their things and go.)

Precious: Did you catch that? *(Staring at them, then looking at Charles again before Mary and Andrews recognise, they've been spotted.)*

Casanova: *(surprised and down.)* I've spotted it, and I have always suspected he's committing infidelity, even seen him but had no proof until now. But please, do not tell anyone this; this shall devastate Charles.

Precious: Wow. *(Impressed.)* You know what can hurt people's feelings? I am amazed.

Casanova: *(Disappointed.)* I am human; what do you take me for?

Precious: I have heard a lot about you.

Casanova: That's the problem; listening to people- you shouldn't do that, but trust in me dear! *(Holding her hands.)* Bringing people into our relationship will preclude it from growing and flowing.

Precious: You are such a smooth talker. *(Blushes).*

Casanova*: (Smiling).* You are so beautiful; I could gaze upon you the whole day. *(They get close.)*

Precious: You are so sweet. *(They kiss.)*

Exeunt

7.2.5 Scene Five

(Silvermine Nature Reserve, which forms part of the Table Mountain National Park[1] in Cape Town[2], South Africa[3]. It covers the section of the Cape Peninsula[4] mountain range from the Kalk Bay[5] Mountains through to Constantia berg. The area is a significant conservation area for the indigenous fynbos[6] vegetation, which is of the montane cone-bush[7] type.

The Ou Kaapse[8] wayside main road runs through the reserve, cutting it into a northern and southern section. The Silvermine reservoir, on the north side, supplies water to Cape Town.

The area is popular for walking, hiking, picnicking, and mountain biking. There are several sandstone cave systems in the reserve, and there are rock climbing routes on Muizenberg Peak.

As the cool breeze of autumn sweeps through the meadow, the vibrant colours of the changing leaves create a beautiful contrast against the clear blue sky.

The tall grasses and wildflowers that once flourished during the summer months now give way to golden-brown hues, with their dried stalks rustling in the wind.

Enter Cynthia and Charles, as the cool breeze rustles through the leaves, creating a symphony of sound as the two teenagers make their way through the meadow.

Cynthia, with her amber-brown long hair tied back in a ponytail, wore a comfortable and stylish outfit that was perfect for the outdoors. Her plaid flannel shirt, paired with dark blue jeans and hiking boots, complemented her natural beauty.

Charles, with his short hair and athletic build, wore a matching flannel shirt, khaki pants, and hiking boots. The couple walks hand in hand, their clothing blending

---

1. https://en.wikipedia.org/wiki/Table_Mountain_National_Park

2. https://en.wikipedia.org/wiki/Cape_Town

3. https://en.wikipedia.org/wiki/South_Africa

4. https://en.wikipedia.org/wiki/Cape_Peninsula

5. https://en.wikipedia.org/wiki/Kalk_Bay

6. https://en.wikipedia.org/wiki/Fynbos

7. https://en.wikipedia.org/wiki/Cone_bush

8. https://en.wikipedia.org/wiki/Ou_Kaapse_Weg

seamlessly with the natural surroundings. They were both clearly excited to be out in nature, enjoying the beauty of the meadow and the fresh autumn air.)

Charles: This is such a beautiful place; I just adore the crystal Silvermine River, which starts in the reserve and runs to Clovelly, the only river in the Cape Peninsula that runs its whole course without going through a developed area.

Cynthia: It is so lovely. Just look at the tall grasses and wildflowers that once flourished during the summer months now give way to golden-brown hues, with their dried stalks rustling in the wind. Take your eyes over there, to that small patch of green remains, as few hardy plants hold on to the last vestiges of their summer glory. The leaves of the oak trees have turned a rich brown, and their acorns fall to the ground with a soft thud.

Charles: The once-lush shrubs and bushes now stand barren, with only a few remaining leaves clinging to their branches. In their place, a variety of mushrooms have sprouted up, their caps ranging in colour from pale white to deep brown. The Silvermine stream is winding its way through the meadow here, its banks lined with stones and fallen leaves. The water trickles gently over the rocks, creating a soothing melody that blends with the rustling of the leaves. Nature is so adorable.

Cynthia: Despite all that, with the signs of the approaching winter, the meadow still teems with life. A variety of birds still flit through the air, their bright feathers a stark contrast against the muted landscape; squirrels scamper across the ground, collecting acorns and other nuts to store away for the colder months.

Charles: Yea, as we are in the second week of April, there have already been signs of new growth; the tiny buds have formed on the trees, and a few braves of flowers have pushed their way up through the ground. The meadow may be quiet and subdued, but it is still full of beauty and life, even as the seasons change.

Cynthia: Spot on. I just enjoy hiking here with you, but you seem to be so down lately.

Charles: I have just been thinking; I even came here to refresh my mind.

Cynthia: What is it?

Charles: It's nothing. Charles seems concerned but afraid to speak out.

Cynthia: You know that; you can tell me anything.

Charles: *(wearily).* It's just something I have been worried about; I do not know if I am overthinking it or what.

Cynthia: (They stop walking for a moment.) Darling, what's on your mind?

Charles: Well, my mother has been away for a while now, and I'm living with my dad. Lately, I've noticed that he's been acting really strange. He doesn't answer my calls or texts like he used to, and my mother has called me to say that she is concerned about the same thing, and I'm worried that he's not doing well.

Cynthia: I'm sorry to hear that, Charles. Have you tried talking to him about it?

Charles: I've tried, but he just brushes me off and says that he's fine. But I know something's not right.

Cynthia: Maybe he's just busy with work or something. You said he's a teacher, right?

Charles: Yeah, but it's not just that. I'm worried that he and my mom aren't communicating like they used to. They've always been really close, but since she's been away, he's just been different. *(They continue walking.)*

Cynthia: *(Clam)* I'm sure they'll work it out, Charles. You can't control their relationship, but you can be there for your dad and support him through whatever he's going through.

Charles: You're right, Cynthia. I just wish I knew what was going on with him.

Cynthia: Just give him time and be patient. I'm sure he'll come around and talk to you when he's ready.

Charles: (Calm.) Thanks, Cynthia. You always know how to make me feel better.

Cynthia: Of course, Charles. I care about you, and I'm here for you no matter what.

Cynthia: Of course, I will always be there for you.

Charles: Where is Precious? I was still waiting to see if she'd go on a date with the bachelor. They stop walking.

Cynthia: I think I made it clear to Bachelor that he cannot date Precious.

Cynthia: What? Why did you do that?

Cynthia: Can't you see? You are dating me, and you are his friend; the Precious is my sister. That is something I cannot allow.

Charles: (Disappointed). Isn't that her choice?

Cynthia: (infuriated.) I know you want your friend to have a girlfriend, but it cannot be my sister. I do not want all the drama. I can't imagine going to see the same men as my sister and talking about the same adventures and explorations.

Charles: (*shocked.*) I did not know you felt like that! Bachelor is a good boy; you'd rather let be with vultures than with him?

Cynthia: It's not about being good or bad; it's about my space, happiness, feelings, and emotions. I do not want to date a man who is a friend of my younger sister's boyfriend. It will not be funny; I want to advise her with different notions and experiences, which is what I want from her as well.

Charles: After all this time, all my efforts were for nothing?

Cynthia: What efforts? (Curious.)

Charles: Never mind. (*He walks away; Cynthia follows.*)

Cynthia: What efforts? (*She pauses*). Wait, are you the one who sent the text to him?

Charles: No (*he avoids eye contact.*)

Cynthia: Ah... Yes, I knew it. I could tell that it was not The Bachelor who sent that.

Charles: I was attempting to assist a friend.

Cynthia: (*Laughs.*) I can't believe it. Your friend needs to be a man. And unfortunately, Precious went on a date with Casanova last week; today, right after school, she went for a coffee with him.

Charles: (Surprised.) And you are telling me this now? Cynthia! I cannot believe you. How can you let her go to that vulture?

Cynthia: I cannot make determinations for her.

Charles: But you have, by precluding Bachelor to date her.

Cynthia: It's different, babe.

Charles: I can't stand you. (*Inflamed.*) You would rather let her be with that dragon than an innocent soul like my friend. You are selfish; you think about yourself and Casanova.

Cynthia: (Angry.) How can you compare such situations? These two situations are incommensurable: Casanova is a boy with some teenage mood problems, and I, on the other side, am concerned about my healthy relationship with you.

Charles: Do you see? It is always: "I, mine, and myself and my." I am done! (*He walks away.*)

Cynthia: What do you mean? (*He follows him.*)

Exeunt

7.2.6 Scene Six

(In the afternoon, Fish Hoek, False Bay College is in Cape Town[1], South Africa[2]. The False Bay TVET College offers vocational, occupational, and skills programs in a range of fields: engineering, business, hospitality, information technology, safety in society, education studies, 2D animation, tourism, and boat building.)

Nicole: Leah, have you heard the news? My sister Sharon just got engaged on Valentine's Day!

Leah: *(trying to hide her disappointment.)* Oh, wow. That's great news for them.

Nicole: *(noting Leah's tone.)* Is everything okay, Leah? You don't sound too thrilled.

Leah: *(sighs.)* Well, I'm happy for Sharon, but I have to admit, it's awkward for me.

Nicole: *(concerned.)* What do you mean, Leah?

Leah: *(hesitantly.)* I was in love with Valentine once. I mean, I tried to break them up once, but it obviously didn't work out.

Nicole: *(surprised.)* What?! I had no idea. When was this?

Leah: *(looking down.)* It was a while ago, when Valentine and Sharon had broken up. I just didn't want to see them together again; you know? But I've moved on from that.

Nicole: *(nodding.)* I understand. But you have to be happy for them, Leah. They're in love, and it's their special day.

Leah: *(nodding reluctantly.)* You're right, Nicole. I am happy for them. It's just that seeing Valentine with Sharon now... brings back some old feelings.

---

1. *https://en.wikipedia.org/wiki/Cape_Town*

2. *https://en.wikipedia.org/wiki/South_Africa*

Nicole: *(concerned.)* What feelings do you have, Leah?

Leah: *(pauses.)* I don't know. I guess I still have feelings for Valentine, but I know it's not right. Sharon is his fiancée now, and I respect that.

Nicole: *(nodding.)* You should, Leah. It's not fair to Sharon or Valentine if you hold on to those feelings. Move on and find someone else who's right for you.

Leah*: (smiling weakly.)* I know, Nicole. I'll try my best to focus on the present and not dwell on the past.

Sharon*: (interrupting their conversation.)* Hey, guys! What are you talking about?

Nicole: *(smiling.)* We were just talking about your engagement, Sharon. **Congratulations!** What brings you here?

Sharon*: (beaming.)* Thank you! I'm so excited. I just came to check on you; I had an early day off.

Leah: *(forcing a smile.)* Yes, congratulations.

Sharon: *(noticing Leah's expression.)* Is everything okay, Leah?

Leah: (nodding.) Yeah, everything's fine. I'm just thrilled for you and Valentine.

Sharon: *(smiling.)* That's good to hear. We're all going to be family soon, so we should celebrate together.

Leah: *(forcing another smile.)* Yes, we should. I'll help with the planning.

Nicole: (grins.) Great! It's going to be an amazing celebration. Well, I am done lecturing for today; let's head home. *(She stands up.)* Are you coming, Leah?

Leah: No, I'll sit a bit; I still have some marking to do, and I don't enjoy marking college work at home. (Fake smile).

Nicole: Cool. See you tomorrow then.

Sharon: Bye.

Sharon and Nicole exeunt

Leah: *(Frustrated and envious.)* I can't even help myself with my jealousy. But what can I do then? Valentine has made his choice, and what we did with him some three years ago can never happen again. Nicole does not even know that. What do I do? I cannot just let Sharon take away my happiness.

Exeunt

7.2.7 Scene Seven

(Green Point an Office, Enter Ntombi and Bachelor; they are wrapping up and getting ready to leave at twilight.)

Bachelor: Do you like your internship so far?

Ntombi: I am really enjoying it.

Bachelor: *(Curious.)* Isn't it constraining for you to have to be at UCT, then come here to work with us?

Ntombi: *(smiling weakly.)* It is a bit. But I want some experience; I do not want to come out of the university with a light CV. You know how these companies are; they seek 3–5 years' work experience for an entry-level job.

Bachelor: But you do not have to leave this late, you can leave at 4:30–5:00 p.m.

Ntombi: *(forcing a smile.)* Cool, I am glad to know.

Bachelor: You do not seem to be your usual self lately; what is it?

Ntombi: *(Concerned and weary.)* Casanova!

Bachelor: *(Sighs.)* Ja! That guy...

Ntombi: What? Do you know something?

Bachelor: (Nervous.) No, not at all.

Ntombi: *(Intense.)* Bachelor, if there is something you know, tell me.

Bachelor: Look, I will not say there is nothing going on or not; you know him, moss: the leopard never changes its spots.

Ntombi: But he promised me

Bachelor: *(Laughing.)* And you believe him? That guy is untrustworthy; he is predictable in that he wills all women by himself.

Ntombi: "(*Attentive* and curious.) I am aware of your feud with him. Which I cannot resonate. You'll speak all the ills about him; do you mean he cannot change?

Bachelor: You have just said it yourself. I will not pretend here that everything is fine. Do not worry, and just stay away from that boy before you get crushed. He even went on a date with...

Ntombi: (*Shocked.*) What!

Bachelor: *(regretfully.)* Forget I said anything. Let's just call it a day.

Valentine enters

Valentine: (Confused.) Is there something wrong? You two seem to be arguing.

Bachelor: *(calmly.)* It's nothing, dear. We were just speaking about some work stuff.

Valentine: *(Curious.)* How's your academic work, Ntombi? Please don't overwork yourself.

Ntombi: Everything is great. Thank you for the opportunity you have given me here.

Bachelor: I forgot to tell you; he is engaged to Sharon.

Ntombi: *(Happily.)* That's marvellous. You complement each other so well. When?

Valentine: It's been weeks. Thank you. I'll leave you too. When you come tomorrow, just; please, work on these. (*Giving her some files.*) Bachelor will assist you with all the quality assurance[1] and data analysis[2]. If you struggle, Marissa will assist and oversee your work at the administration and information office.

Ntombi: *(Smiling)*. Cool. (*Valentine goes*). Haha... (*Playing, hitting him with files.*) Why did you not tell me your brother is engaged?

---

1.   https://en.wikipedia.org/wiki/Quality_assurance

2.   https://en.wikipedia.org/wiki/Data_analysis

Bachelor: I am sorry; it might have flipped my mind. I have also been going through a lot. I have been thinking of doing something for them.

Ntombi: Like an engagement party?

Bachelor: Yea, even though it's not a party but something small to celebrate with them.

Ntombi: Lovely, I can help you arrange that.

Bachelor: (*Smiling.*) Thank you.

Exeunt

7.2.8 Scene Eight

(At dusk, the sun has set on the horizon; leaving behind vibrant colours painted in shades of pink, orange, and red; The air is cool and crisp, with a gentle breeze rustling through the trees; which have been withering; with leaves turning shades of gold, orange, and red, and the sky in a deep shade of blue, with a few wispy clouds fading away; The stars in the constellation appear bit by bit; starting with the brighter ones and followed by lesser ones as the sky is turning deep navy. Enter Valentine and Max.)

MAX: So you are tying the knot soon?

Valentine: "Yes, buddy."

Max: (*Happily.*) I am so happy for you; I'm just saddened we shall no longer be able to stuff as much into our leisure time as we used to.

Valentine: Why not? We shall continue to be friends, and what we have been doing, we shall continue.

Max: (*Laughing.*) No, because you don't want to instil unnecessary insecurities in your wife now that you're a husband.

Valentine: (*Sighs.*) You have a point there.

Max: Hey Valentine, I'm doing well. You're looking sharp in that Audi. When did you get it?

Valentine: Thanks, man. I've had it for a few months now. It's the latest 2010 model.

Max: Nice, it looks really sleek. And how's life at the mansion? I'm sure it's treating you well.

Valentine: Life's good, can't complain. The mansion is fine, but I like having my own space. Plus, it's nice to be able to entertain guests and throw parties.

Max: Yeah, I can imagine. You're really living the high life, man. I have to say, I'm inspired by your success.

Valentine: Thanks, Max. I've worked hard to get where I am today.

Max: I can tell. But tell me, what's your secret? How did you become so successful?

Valentine: Well, it's not really a secret, but I inherited my family's wine company when my parents died. I took control of if as years passed, when my uncle retired.

Max: Ah, I see. That's definitely a great starting point.

Valentine: Yeah, it definitely helps. But there's something I need to tell you. It's something that few people know.

Max: What is it?

Valentine: My younger brother had a twin.

Max: What? I did not know. What happened to him?

Valentine: He got kidnapped when we were kids. Our parents were murdered, and we lost him in the chaos.

Max: Oh my god, that's terrible. I did not know.

Valentine: Yeah, it was a really difficult time for my family. We've never been able to find out what happened to him, and we don't even know if he's still alive.

Max: I'm so sorry to hear that, Valentine. That must have been really hard for you and your family.

Valentine: It was, but we've learnt to live with it. I just hope that someday, we'll be able to find out what happened to him and maybe even bring him back home.

Max: I hope so too, man. And if there's ever anything I can do to help, please ask.

Valentine: Thanks, Max. I really appreciate that. I am just concerned about him when he finds out we told him half-truth.

Max: What do you mean?

Valentine: He knows how we lost our parents, but we thought it would devastate him more if we told him he had a twin. I now feel so guilty.

Max*: (Sad.)* That must be hard, but in the end, tell him, for the truth has a way of revealing itself.

Exeunt

7.2.9 Scene Nine

(In the evening, there is a cool breeze from the sea, the sky is dark, with a variety of stars across; enter Cynthia and Precious, Fish Hoek, a family home.)

Precious*: (Curious.)* So how was your hiking with Charles? It must have been fun.

Cynthia: (Sighs.) I so wish—at first glance, it was so fun; we were so connected, adoring the beauty of nature until Bachelor's name came. What's wrong with him?

Precious: (Concerned.) What happened?

Cynthia: *(inflamed.)* We ended up fighting and arguing. He even had the nerve to tell me I was selfish. Am I selfish?

Precious: (surprised.) Tell me what happened.

Cynthia: This whole situation-involving you, Bachelor, and Casanova. I did not point with a gun that to go on a date with Casanova, I just said do not date Bachelor since he is Charles' friend.

Precious: *(wearily.)* And he doesn't see it that way?

Cynthia: Yes, I so wish someone could talk some sense into him. The worst part is, he is not even innocent here, and he is the one who sent you the text, pretending to be Bachelor.

Precious: *(Shocked.)* What! So all this time I have been chatting with Bachelor?

Cynthia: I don't know; it seems so; but I am certain of the last text Bachelor sent you: it was not from him but Charles. I know how he writes.

Precious: *(sighs.)* I don't even know what to say. How can I be fooled like this?

Cynthia: (Angrily.) What pisses me off, Charles seems to be more concerned about his friend's emotions than mine. How can that be? I am his girlfriend. I should be first in his priorities, not Bachelor.

Precious: *(Calm.)* I am sorry to hear this; this is all my fault.

Cynthia: (perplexed.) How is it your fault? You made your own choice. I even warned you about him, but you said you want to make your own determinations and mistakes and learn from them. My only sin is to support my sister in fulfilling her desires.

Precious: *(eagerly.)* I need to speak some sense to him, and tell Bachelor that what he did uncalled for. He needs to man up.

Cynthia: No, do not do that; you shall just add fuel to the fire.

Precious: No, I have to do this. We can't let men think they can control and manipulate us like this; thereafter, we'll be chasing after them.

Cynthia: Your feminist approach will not mend this situation. Just let it go; Charles shall come around, and I'll talk to him.

Precious: *(concerned.)* And if he does not?

Cynthia: He will, just do not escalate the situation, I would not want to lose Charles.

Precious: Robert truly ripped your heart, seeing that you are so fond of Charles, you cannot even see something beyond him; he is a warm-hearted man indeed.

Cynthia: *(looking at her straight in the eyes.)* Can you see now?

Precious: Fine, I shall not talk to him, but I shall speak to Bachelor. I cannot let this go; and I do not want him to think I have blue-tacked him.

Cynthia: (*Calm.*) I wish you the best on that.

Precious: *(thinking and recalling.)* Hey, I forgot to tell you something.

Cynthia: *(Curious.)* What is it?

Precious: This will cripple your heart, too. I am so worried.

Cynthia: What is it? (*Opening eyes wide.*) Tell me!

Precious: I was at a coffee shop today, with Casanova; we caught Mr Andrews cheating on his wife.

Cynthia: What! (*Shocked.*) There is no way! Please tell me you are joking.

Precious: I am dead serious. Look... (*She takes out her cell phone and shows it to her.*)

Cynthia: (*Frowning.*) No way! (Shivering.) This can't be happening. And why did you take a picture? Do you know what this means?

Precious: What?

Cynthia: Charles has been concerned about his parents, that they are so disconnected; this is the reason; but also, you have this picture; any mistake will rip that family apart. I would not want that. It would devastate Charles. So whatever games you were thinking of, delete this.

Precious: No!

Cynthia: What do you mean by "no?

Precious: I wanted to use it as leverage in case I fail his accounting.

Cynthia: (angrily.) I can't believe you said that! Just study, practice, practice, and you shall pass. Not this. This is being selfish and not thinking about the ramifications of what this would do. It would tear a family apart. Do you want that?

Precious. (*Concerned.*) No.

Cynthia: Then, please. Delete this. Remove it from the bin or trash. Give me the cell phone. (Precious resists). Give me the cell phone. Imagine if this were to happen in our family and it ripped us apart.

Precious: (curious.) So, you would rather let our mother not know if she cheated on our father.

Cynthia: I think some incidents and secrets should remain sealed for us to live in peace and be in intimate communion. Imagine if all secrets can be revealed? They would rip apart families, divorces, would come, children would rise in foster homes, it would kill people, brothers would rise against each other; kindred against kindred, neighbours against neighbours.

Precious: (*Convinced.*) Okay, if you say so. *(She deletes it while Cynthia is looking.)*

Exeunt

7.2.10 Scene Ten

(In the evening, Andrews and Paul walk into a nightclub.)

Paul: (Curious). You are not your usual self today. What is it?

Andrews: (Sighs.) I am just thinking; I have been thinking.

Paul: (attentively.) I am all ears.

Andrews: I have been thinking about my marriage, Charles' mother, and then there is Marry.

Paul: (intense.) You seem to be so concerned.

Charles: (Pours a whisky.) I am. (He drinks). My wife will be here in a few days. I am nervous, and we have not been intimate in a long time, so we feel disconnected.

Paul: So, what are you going to do now with Mary?

Andrews: *(ponders.)* I do not know, my friend, maybe we should take a break or something.

Paul: But this wouldn't work. You need to call off things before it is too late; she is even your colleague.

Andrews: I am having an intra conflict with myself-my conscience tells me I must dump her and call it quits, moreover; there is still that demon that says no, you attain so much pleasure and fun from her, far outweighing your wife.

Paul: You see... That is something you should pray for and fast. Read your Bible; refute it.

Andrews: (Laughs.) As if you do that?

Paul: Please, let's not even get there.

Andrews: I hope she doesn't find out.

Paul: She won't unless you tell her.

Andrews: Really?

Paul: We have been friends for three decades now; we met when we were 20 years old. Have we ever been caught in our infidelity?

Andrews: Yea, for that I can attest. But then, technology has changed; you might never know.

Exeunt

7.2.11 Scene Eleven

(Hout Bay, Enter Rose, in a garage, at a petrol station)

Rose: *(Frustrated.)* I really hate this guy; I can't stand him, and how could he stoop me up like this? It's 9:00 p.m. I don't even know what I am going to say at home. I am going to expose him; just because I got into this mess knowingly does not mean he must treat me like crap. Bachelor, you better come; you are my only hope. (A black Mercedes Benz, arrives.) This must be you. *(She goes it).*

Bachelor: *(Opens the door.)* Hey, how are you doing?

Rose: "I am cold." *(Getting inside the car)*

Bachelor: *(Curious.)* What is it?

Rose: (Angrily). That trash stood me up. I have been here for him for hours, and he did not pitch.

Bachelor: *(Confused.)* Who?

Rose: Casanova, whom do you think?

Bachelor: *(calmly, and laughing.)* You got yourself into this entanglement with Casanova as well?

Rose: You are laughing at me.

Bachelor: *(Intense.)* I just don't understand you guys. Ntombi was just complaining about him to me just now; now it's you; He had also taken Precious on a date.

Rose: Casanova went on a date with Precious?

Bachelor: Yes, Rose, I had asked her on a date, and she chose him.

Rose: I knew Casanova is in a relationship with Ntombi and another girl, but Precious...

Bachelor: *(shocked.)* You knew? I can't believe it. Why would you do that?

Rose: I just... I'm not sure why I wanted to see what all the girls in him did.

Bachelor: And now?

Rose: (*Frustrated.*) I think I have loved him for now. My God, how did I get myself into this mess? He and I had agreed that we would just have a good time together, but now...

Bachelor: Do you see how selfish he is? That guy has no good intentions about anyone but himself and gratifying his sexual urges, which I can't comprehend why you girls are so lured into him.

Rose: Let me tell you something. He may toy with us, but he does the most amazing things for us that most guys who are loyal cannot. He gives you time... (*Bachelor disturbs her.*)

Bachelor: Has he given you now?

Rose: Wait, let me finish. Casanova has that irresistibility; he may not be the most handsome guy around, but the way he dresses, the way he talks, the way he gives you attention, he doesn't even question your whereabouts, and he is so understanding of what girls need. He is a good kisser and can make love so well. He is so funny, you can have a nice, flowing conversation with him. He has a style of dressing and a unique way of approaching a woman; you just feel so elated when you are with him. There is a good heart in him; it's just that he is womaniser; he has tainted himself with all that; otherwise, if he could stop all that, you'd see a good man. He has also been so willing to find out about his real parents since he was adopted.

Bachelor: (*shocked.*) What!

Rose: Yes, hardly anyone knows that; I've only mentioned it to one friend of mine at Fish School High School.

Bachelor: I see. But what he is doing is wrong.

Rose: Yes, and for that, I am going to confront Precious, and tell her to stay away from him.

Bachelor: (*Curious.*) Let me get this straight. So, you are going to confront her, while you, yourself; do not even know where you stand with him? Remember, there is also Ntombi.

Rose: I shall take it from there; at least I know what I am getting myself into.

Bachelor: (*Sleepy.*) It's late, and I am so exhausted. I am tired of having to even drive you to Fish Hoek FET College now to your residence. Why don't you sleep at my place, then I'll take you tomorrow morning then?

Rose: Where shall I sleep?

Bachelor: Don't worry, there are plenty of bedrooms in that mansion. I also don't think my brother would be around tonight, so no one will be suspicious.

Rose: Okay, thank you.

Exeunt

7.2.12 Scene Twelve

(The following day, at noon; enter Ntombi and Casanova, UCT, a restaurant.)

Ntombi: *(Frustrated.)* You've been avoiding me lately; I can't even reach you on the phone or in my Facebook inbox.

Casanova: *(nervously.)* I am sorry, I have just been busy.

Ntombi: *(Angrily.)* Busy with what? Busy with what? Tell me!

Casanova: What's going on, and why are you so inflamed?

Ntombi: Don't you dare, fool me! Who is the girl you went on a date with?

Casanova: *(feeling guilty and shocked.)* What girl? What are you talking about?

Ntombi: You thought I would not know? You thought I would not find out?

Casanova: Who told you that?

Ntombi: Bachelor told me you went on a date with someone, not out of spite, but because it slipped his tongue.

Casanova: Of course, it had to be him. That dude will never let me be at peace with my life. I can't stand him. I'll sort him out.

Ntombi: No, don't dare. Don't blame him for everything when it's your fault.

Casanova: Maybe I did, went to a luncheon with someone, but it wasn't a date. Have I disappointed you in the past? Have I not given you time and fulfilment?

Ntombi: *(seems to be convinced.)* You have started now to shift away from that, and I am no longer getting your time as usual.

Casanova: I just had a lot on my plate, doing all the hotel stuff, driving up and down in Fish Hoek, Hout Bay, and Cape Town central.

Ntombi: You better not be lying to me, because I will find out if you are!

Casanova: No, I am not, darling. I love you; you know that. Even if I may be with a side chick, you are the one.

Ntombi: *(shocked and curious.)* What the hell are you saying?

Casanova: I am saying, "You shall always be the one." Girls may approach me, but you are the one; I have not been perfect; I have cheated on you; I acknowledge that and have apologised; you have made me a better person who understands the value of another person's emotions.

Ntombi: "Okay, I hope you are not lying to me."

Casanova: I am not.

Ntombi: I need to go now. *(Checking time.)* I have some lecture sessions right now.

Casanova: Cool. *(Trying to kiss her)*

Ntombi: Not in public. I don't want everyone's eyes on me. I'll see you.

Casanova: *(Disappointed.)* Cool. *(They stand up, embrace each other).* Goodbye, I'll see you.

Ntombi: Bye. *(She goes.)*

Casanova: (sits down.) That son of a... I am going to kill him. I almost got caught today. Maybe this must end. My lies are piling up, but why focus on one girl? Can I do that? What would it take from me? But I have so much fun doing what I am doing: moreover, at what cost? I don't know which of these I truly love or which I enjoy being with the most. I need to find myself. Look deep so I can see. But Bachelor, I'll show him what makes the grass green. ***Exit***

7.2.13 Scene Thirteen

(Fish Hoek, High School, enter Marry and Andrews, during break time, Mr. Andrews' Class.)

Marry: You cannot believe how much I have missed you.

Andrews: Me too; I have missed you so much. (*He kisses her.*) But now it's going to be difficult.

Marry: How? (*Confused.*)

Andrews: We can't carry on like this. People are getting suspicious of our cosiness, in particular here at school.

Marry: (*in agreement.*) Yea, we've got to be careful, us playing hide and seek here at school will get us caught.

Andrews: Yes, so let's not get too cosy here. (*In thought.*) I almost forgot to tell you something.

Marry: What is it?

Andrews: Charles' mother, my wife, is coming back soon. I would not want her to find out about us.

Marry: She shall not, as long as we are cautious.

Andrews: I thought maybe we should take a break.

Marry: (*Surprised.*) What! Are you dumping me, Andrews?

Andrews: No, it's just that...

Marry: It's just what?

Andrews: Can't you see? (*Opening eyes wide.*) You told me your husband was coming soon, and he is the guy who doesn't inform but surprises.

Marry: Yea, you have a point there. I just like you. I enjoy your company.

Andrews: They touch each other's hands. (*Charles enters, they refrain instantly and are frighten.*)

Charles: Good afternoon.

Marry: *(Mumbling).* How are you?

Charles: I am fine, and you, Mrs. Tshawe?

Marry: How's your mother?

Charles: She is well. I was just speaking to her over the cell phone, and she's coming soon.

Marry: (faking a smile.) That's great. Say hi to her. Let me go, to let you catch up. *(She goes).*

Andrews: What brings you here, son?

Charles: I wasn't doing anything, so I thought I should bring you some luncheon. *(He puts some takeaway on the desk and sits.)*

Andrews: Thank you very much.

Charles: *(They eat.)* I have missed you, dad. Sometimes you don't sleep at home these days. What is it?

Andrews: *(guiltiness.)* Nothing. I just wanted some fresh air; I did not want those walls to keep reminding me of your mother.

Charles: *(confused.)* What? But that is our home, father. Shouldn't it be so?

Andrews: No, not like that. I have just been distressed with work, our financial issues, and your mother's absence. I did not want to bother you; see how distressed I am.

Charles: But I am old now, dad; I might be 19 years old, but do not keep me in the dark.

Andrews: Cool. How's college?

Charles: It's going pretty well. Nicole Michelson is such a good lecturer; she's a sister to Sharon, who is engaged to Valentine's brother. They are fortunate. The Green family is so rich.

Andrews: Don't yearn to be in the upper class; the middle class you are in is fine. There are even millions of people in far worse situations than us. Think about the black people in previously independent homelands like Transkei and Ciskei; many of them have fled to here, and still come in numbers- look at the informal settlements around the City of Cape Town Municipality.

Charles: Yes, you have a point there.

Andrews: I am glad you can see Charles Andrews.

Exeunt

7.2.14 Scene Fourteen

(Enter Precious and Bachelor: Bachelor is driving a 2010 A4 sedan, wagon, and Precious is walking on the pavement, while Bachelor is driving slowly; it is a few minutes after school, other students are leaving school, and there are some vehicles taking some pupils from the school)

Bachelor: Hi Precious, can we talk for a moment?

Precious: Sure, what's up?

Bachelor: Can you get inside the car?

Precious: No, I am fine; just talk.

Bachelor: Precious, please, this is unsafe.

Precious: Okay. *(Precious gets inside a passenger seat.)*

Bachelor: How are you?

Precious: I am fine.

Bachelor: I am fine too.

Precious: Is that all?

Bachelor: I heard from Cynthia that you're in a relationship with Casanova. Is that true?

Precious: Yes, it is.

Bachelor: I have to say I'm disappointed. We had plans to go out on a date, and you went out with Casanova instead.

Precious: I'm sorry, Bachelor, but I didn't know you were interested in me that way. I thought we were just friends.

Bachelor: I asked you out on a date, Precious. What else could that mean?

Precious: Look, Bachelor, I'm sorry for not realizing your intentions, but you have to understand that I'm in a relationship now, and I'm happy with Casanova.

Bachelor: But Precious, you know his reputation. He's known for playing girls and hurting them.

Precious: I know his reputation, and I know he's been with a lot of girls, but he's been nothing but kind and respectful towards me.

Bachelor: But what about the other girls? He's hurt? Don't you care about that?

Precious: Of course I do, Bachelor. But I'm not them. I don't know what happened between Casanova and those girls, and I will not judge him based on his past.

Bachelor: I just don't want to see you get hurt, Precious. You deserve someone who will treat you with respect and love.

Precious: I appreciate your concern, Bachelor, but I don't need your protection. I can take care of myself.

Bachelor: I'm not trying to protect you, Precious. I just care about you, and I don't want to see you get hurt.

Precious: Well, I will not get hurt, Bachelor. Casanova is different with me, and I trust him.

Bachelor: Fine, but I just want to know one thing. Did you receive a message from me on Facebook asking you out on a date?

Precious: Yes, I did, but I knew it wasn't from you. Your friend Charles sent it, didn't he?

Bachelor: Yes, he did. I'm sorry about that. He thought it would be funny.

Precious: Funny? That's not funny, Bachelor. That's disrespectful and immature.

Bachelor: I know, and I apologize. It was wrong of him to do that.

Precious: I just can't believe you would associate yourself with someone who would do something like that.

Bachelor: I'm sorry, Precious. I shouldn't have let him do it.

Precious: It's too late for apologies, Bachelor. I don't want to talk to you right now.

Bachelor: I understand, Precious. I'll leave you alone.

Precious: Great. Can I get out of the vehicle now?

Bachelor: I can take you home.

Precious: No thanks.

Bachelor: Okay. *(He stops the car, then opens the door for her. Precious gets off the vehicle.)*

Precious: Bye. Wait... by the way, you came all the way here to see me?

Bachelor: I had to drop Rose by. She slept at my place.

Precious: What! *(Shocked.)* Why?

Bachelor: No, it's not what you think. Just ask your boyfriend.

Precious: What do you mean?

Bachelor: Goodbye. *(Precious is left puzzled, and Bachelor shuts the door. Bachelor is driving, with his thoughts swirling in his head. He sighs heavily and speaks aloud to himself.)*

Alas, what a cruel fate befalls me! The girl I had my heart set on, the one I hoped to finally go on a date with, has fallen for that Casanova. The same Casanova who has toyed with the hearts of countless women before her. And yet, here I am, still alone, with no one to call my own. I had hoped that this girl might be different, that she might see something in me that no one else ever has. But no, she, too, has fallen under his spell. What is it about him that draws women to him like moths to a flame? Is it his charm, his good looks, his smooth talking ways? Or is it simply the thrill of the chase, the excitement of being with someone who is so well known as a player? I cannot help but feel hurt by this, for I have never had a girlfriend before.

This was my last hope, my chance to experience what it's like to be with someone I truly care for. And now, it's all been dashed to pieces. As I drive, I can't help but wonder if I will ever find love. Will I forever be alone, watching from the side-lines as others find happiness with someone they love? Or will I one day find my own sweetheart, someone who sees in me what others do not? Only time will tell, but for now, I am left to ponder what could have been, and to nurse the wounds of a heart that has been shattered once again.

(As the car disappears, Precious is left puzzled, and confused.)

Precious: (walking on the pavement.) What did Bachelor mean? Rose slept at his place. When I ask, he says I must ask my boyfriend? *(In a moment, a car stops by, it is driven by Casanova.)*

Casanova: Hey, beautiful (smiling.)

Precious: (*Excited.*) Hi, honey.

Casanova: Get inside, please. *(Precious gets inside the passenger seat.)* How have you been?

Precious: I am well, babe, and I am just thrilled to see you. (They embrace.) But then... I was just with Bachelor just now.

Casanova: (*Ponders.*) What about him?

Precious: It's not important anymore; I made it clear what I wanted—you. Something shut me off, and I am still puzzled.

Casanova: (*Curious.*) What is it?

Precious: Apparently, Rose slept at Bachelor's house last night. He came all the way from to drop her here in Fish-Hoek.

Casanova: (shocked.) What? How is that even possible?

Precious: Bachelor. He said it is not what I think, but I must ask you. *(Looking at him directly.)* You tell me, what's going on?

Casanova: (feeling guilty) I don't know what he meant. Don't take him seriously.

Precious: I did not say I take him seriously, but I was just wondering why he would say that.

Casanova: Darling, you know that I and he are opposed to one another. We are east and west. That guy shall do anything to taint my name. I am fun, glittering, and spontaneous; I draw many people, which is something he may never have. Don't listen to him; he'll do anything out of spite to ruin my happiness-our happiness.

Precious: Okay, if you say so.

Casanova: (Relieved.) Yes, darling. So, how was your day? *(He starts the car and drives.)*

Precious: It was marvellous. (Smiling.)

Casanova: Same as mine. I love you.

Precious: I love you too.

Exeunt

7.2.15 Scene Fifteen

(Fish Hoek, A Family Home, enter Mollie, Sharon, and Nicole.)

Mollie: Sharon, my dear, I am so thrilled about your engagement! I can't wait to plan the wedding.

Sharon: Thank you, Mom. Me too, I'm so agitated.

Nicole: *(rolling her eyes.)* Here we go again.

Mollie: Nicole, what's the matter? You don't seem very excited about your sister's engagement.

Nicole: I'm happy for her, Mom, but I'm just not that interested in marriage.

Mollie: *(surprised.)* What do you mean you're not interested in marriage? You're not getting any younger, Nicole.

Nicole: *(frustrated.)* I know, Mom. But getting married isn't the only path to happiness.

Mollie: *(disappointed.)* But it's a big part of life, Nicole. Don't you want to settle down and start a family someday?

Nicole: *(smiling.)* Mom, I have a great job and a wonderful group of friends. I'm happy just the way I am.

Mollie: *(sighing.)* I suppose I just want the best for both of my daughters. Sharon, I'm so happy for you, and Nicole, I just want you to be happy, too.

Sharon: *(grins.)* Don't worry, Mom. I'm sure Nicole will find her own way.

Nicole: *(nodding.)* Exactly. Thanks, Sharon.

Mollie: Is that what you want? Really?

Nicole: *(sighing.)* Mom, I'm happy with my life right now. Marriage isn't a priority for me.

Mollie: (*disappointed.*) But don't you want to find someone to settle down with and start a family?

Nicole: (*shrugging.*) I'm not sure if that's what I want for my life. Plus, not everyone needs to follow the same path to happiness.

Mollie: (*nodding.*) I guess you're right. I just want the best for both of you.

Nicole: (*smiling.*) I know you do, Mom.

Mollie: Let me go take a nap; I am just exhausted. Exit

Nicole: (*turning to Sharon.*) Hey, Sharon, can I talk to you for a second? I have something to tell you.

Sharon: (*confused but interested.*) Sure, what's up?

Nicole: (*whispering.*) Remember when you met me and my friend at Fish College?

Sharon: Yes. (*Curious*).

Nicole: I am sensing something from my friend, do you know her?

Sharon: No. What is it?

Nicole: Never mind, let's just talk about your upcoming wedding.

Sharon: "Nicole, what is it?"

Nicole: (*staring at her directly at her eyes.*) Just love Valentine. The step you have taken now is the beginning of a long journey.

Sharon: (*nodding.*) Is there something you are not telling me?

Nicole: (*Sighing.*) Not at all, dear. (*Smiling.*) I am just so elated by you.

Sharon: Thank you.

Exeunt

7.2.16 Scene Sixteen

(Valentine sat in his office, looking over the final figures of the financial statements and budget. He feels relieved that everything is s falling into place, and he couldn't help but smile as he thought about his recent engagement to Sharon. As he leaned back in his chair, he had a soliloquy about how happy he was with his life and how everything seemed to go his way.)

Valentine leans back in his chair, and smiles. I can't believe how lucky I am *(he thinks to himself.)* I have a great job; the company is doing well, and I'm engaged to the woman of my dreams. Everything is perfect. *(Suddenly, the door to his office burst open, and Valentine jumped in surprise. Standing in front of him was Leah, his former lover, whom he had not seen in three years.)*

Leah: Valentine, I can't believe it's you! She exclaimed, her face wide with delight.)

Valentine: *(shocked, unsure of how to react.)* What brings you here? *(He stands.)*

Leah: *(Calm.)* It's been years, and this is how you greet an old friend?

Valentine: Leah, what are you doing here? *(His voice is slightly shaking.)*

Leah: I heard you are engaged. I had hopes for you; you went straight back to her. I had to come see you. (Leah is walking towards him.) I had to congratulate you in person.

Valentine: *(Frustrated, and his mind is racing.)*Really? *(In thought, I wish I had confessed to Sharon about her when the time was right.).*

(Firmly): Leah, you shouldn't be here! I'm engaged to Sharon now, and I want nothing to jeopardize that.

Leah: *(Her face falls, and she takes a step back.)* I understand, Val *[she says softly]*. I just wanted to see you one last time.

Valentine: *(pang of guilt.)* Just go.

Leah: *(Calmly and smiling, she gives him a hug.)* Goodbye.

(Valentine watches Leah as he walks out of his office.)

Valentine: *(Frustrated.)* I should have confessed to Sharon when our relationship was in crisis, the moment we came back together and fixed things. But then, I said she does not have to know her as long as we are back together. *(He closes his eyes and takes a deep breath, then sits down.)*

Exit

7.2.17 Scene Seventeen

(Fish Hoek Beach, Cynthia is standing on the seashore, the sound of waves crashing on the beach providing a soothing background to her thoughts. It's mid-autumn, and the sun is setting over the Atlantic Ocean, casting a golden hue over the beach).

Cynthia*: [sighs deeply].* This place is so beautiful, but my heart is in turmoil. I can't help but worry about my relationship with Charles. We've been together for two years now, but things haven't been the same lately. It's like we're drifting apart, and I don't know what to do. *[She takes a step forward and feels the cool water of the ocean wash over her toes.]*

Cynthia: Maybe I should talk to Charles about what's been bothering me. But I fear how he'll react. What if he gets angry or defensive? What if he doesn't believe me?

[She looks out at the horizon, lost in thought.]

Cynthia: And then there's the other thing. I've been keeping a secret from Charles, and it's eating me up inside. His father, Andrews, is cheating on his mother with a colleague of his, Marry. Precious caught them together at a restaurant last week, and it was obvious what was going on. *[She wrings her hands nervously.]*

Cynthia: I don't know what to do about that either. Should I tell Charles? It could destroy his family, and I don't want to be responsible for that. But he deserves to know the truth.

[She closes her eyes and takes a deep breath, feeling the breeze on her face.]

Cynthia: Maybe I should just enjoy the moment and forget about my problems for a while. But I know I can't do that. These issues are weighing heavily on me, and I need to find a way to resolve them.

(She opens her eyes and looks out at the sea, determined.)

Cynthia: I'll figure it out. I'll talk to Charles, and hopefully he will understand why I do not want Bachelor to date Precious; then we can work on our relationship together, and maybe we'll come out stronger on the other side.

(She smiles to herself and takes another step forward, feeling the water rush over her feet.)

Cynthia: But for now, I'll just enjoy the beauty of this place and the peace it brings.

(She stands there for a moment, taking in the view, before turning and walking back up the beach, ready to face whatever challenges lay ahead; looking out at the sea, lost in thought. It's mid-autumn, and the sun is setting over the ocean, casting a warm glow over the sand).

Cynthia: (*to* herself.) I can't keep this secret from Charles any longer. He deserves to know the truth about his father and what he's been doing with Marry. But I fear how he'll react. What if he doesn't believe me? What if he blames me for destroying his family? *(She takes a deep breath and closes her eyes, feeling the cool breeze on her face.)*

Cynthia: But I can't keep living with this burden. I have to tell Charles the truth and let him decide what to do with it. He's my partner, and I owe him honesty and loyalty.

(As she speaks, a figure suddenly appears behind her. She jumps in surprise and turns around to see Bachelor standing there.)

Bachelor: (*in shock.*) Hey!

Cynthia: (**freighted.**)How long have you been standing up behind me? *(Cynthia is taken aback, realizing that Bachelor must have overheard her talking to herself about the affair.)*

Bachelor: (*fell guilty.*) I just came now. I tried to call your name, but you couldn't hear because of the raging waters from the sea.

Cynthia: Did you hear anything? What brings you here? Shouldn't you be doing some duty for your company?

Bachelor: I do not have **a** company; **it's a** family business.

Cynthia: All the same. *(Notices Bachelor's curiosity facial expression.)* What is it?

Bachelor: I wanted to take some fresh air, but I partially heard what you were saying.

Cynthia: /nervously.) What?

Bachelor: Marry and Andrews' affair.

Cynthia: *(nervously.)* O God, no! No more people must hear this..

Bachelor: *(curious.)* Who else knows it?

Cynthia: *(confessing.)* Casanova and Precious, caught them live at a restaurant, and it was pretty clear what was going on between them.

[Bachelor's expression turns serious as he listens to Cynthia's confession.]

Bachelor: *[shocked.]* Wow, are you sure about this?

Cynthia: *(nodding.)* Yes, I'm sure. They even took a picture of them kissing.

Bachelor: *(thoughtfully.)* This is big. Where is it?

Cynthia: I deleted it. I did not want Charles to find out.

Bachelor: *(sighs.)* Thank goodness. Charles can't know about this. It would devastate him.

Cynthia: *(nods, feeling relieved to have someone to confide in.)* We have to be careful how we approach this.

Bachelor: That is what I think too, that he cannot know this.

Bachelor: We have been at each other's throats, but at least there is something we agree upon.

Cynthia: Yea.

Bachelor: How are things with Charles?

Cynthia: *(rolling eyes.)* They are fine.

Bachelor: *(Looking at her.)* Your face says the opposite.

Cynthia: I do not want to talk about it now, let alone with you. You and he are friends, and there would have to be someone more neutral and pragmatic between us.

Bachelor: *(Sighs).* I see... (They look at each other, standing on the beach, watching the sunset over the ocean, ready to face whatever challenges lie ahead.) Suddenly Casanova arrives.

Casanova: *(Laughing.)* Hi guys.

Cynthia: Hello, what brings you here?

Casanova: I just came here to get some fresh air. *(Starring at Bachelor.)* I just dropped Precious off a few hours ago at Spar on Ivanhoe Road. She wanted to get something there and head home.

Cynthia: Okay, great. *(Smiling.)* Let me go. I hope she has cooked before mom comes from work at False Bay Hospital.

Casanova: Oh yes, she told me that your mother is a doctor. Bye.

Cynthia goes

Casanova: Bachelor, can't you get it in your head that you lost the date to me? And stop causing me problems?

Bachelor: Yeah, I did. But I'm not surprised. You're always trying to take every girl I show an interest in, even Ntombi. You took her.

Casanova: That's not true. I just happen to be more charming and irresistible than you. But that's not why I'm here to talk to you today. Why did you talk to Ntombi about me going on a date with Precious?

Bachelor: What are you talking about? I said nothing to Ntombi. I might have mentioned a date, but not a name, even if I did, so what?

Casanova: *(harshly.)* You shouldn't have said or asked anything about my dates! What's worse, just now; you did same thing with Precious-sabotaging my relationship with her. That was so low, you shouldn't have brought Rose into this. Rose and I know where we stand!

Bachelor: What's the big deal?

(As they are arguing, a stranger in his late 50s stands by listening to them.)

Casanova: The big deal is that you're trying to sabotage my chances with Precious. You're just upset that she chose me over you.

Bachelor: That's not true. I don't care about Precious. And besides, you're the one who's always manipulating girls and playing games.

Casanova: That's rich coming from you. You're the one who slept with Rose while she was still my girlfriend.

Bachelor: Rose slept at my place because you stood her up. I found her stranded at the garage in Hout Bay. I drove her back to Fish Hoek College today. I didn't, and even if I did, it wouldn't matter. You're always dating multiple girls at once, so why can't I?

Casanova: Because you're not as smooth as me. You're just a loser who can't handle the competition.

(the stranger approaches them.)

Stranger: Excuse me, sons. Why are you arguing like this?

Casanova: Mind your own business, sir.

Bachelor: No, it's fine. We're just having a disagreement.

Stranger: You both look so much alike. Are you brothers?

Casanova: What? No way.

Bachelor: That's ridiculous.

Stranger: Are you sure? Because you have the same eyes, nose, and jawline.

Casanova: I don't know what you're talking about.

Bachelor: Neither do I.

Stranger: Well, it's possible that you two were separated at birth. Maybe that's why you're so similar.

Casanova: That's crazy talk.

Bachelor: Yeah, it is. We're not related.

Stranger: Maybe you're not, but you might want to look into it. You could miss out on a relationship with your long-lost brother.

Casanova: I doubt it, but thanks for the suggestion.

Bachelor: Yeah, thanks.

Stranger: No problem. Now, why don't you two shake hands and make up?

Casanova: Alright, fine. *(Shakes Bachelor shakes his hand.)*

Bachelor: *(shaking Casanova's hand.)* Are we cool?

Casanova: Yeah, we're cool. *(As they are shaking hands, there is that magnet that entangles them, preventing them from breaking away from each other.)*

Bachelor: Alright then. I'm out of here.

Casanova: (Sighs.) What a weird conversation.

Stranger: It's always good to keep an open mind. You never know what life might have in store for you.

Casanova: I guess you're right. Thanks for the advice.

Stranger: No problem. Have a good day. You seem to have some deep connection. *(Looking at their entangled hands.).*

Casanova: You too. *(They break away.)*

The stranger walks away.

Bachelor: (Confused.) What was that about?

Casanova: (Puzzled.) I don't know.

Exeunt

7.2.18 Scene Eighteen

(Green Point, a family home, there is a cool breeze, though stars are adorning the sky. Their light across the heavens is disturbed by light pollution in the city; enter Valentine, Bachelor, Sharon, and Nicole, sitting on a table having supper, just outside the mansion, near the swimming pool.)

Bachelor: This is such a nice view. I adore looking at the heavens at night. Unfortunately, there is too much light pollution to be able to gaze up at the stars.

Sharon: True indeed, I always do that when there is load shedding. You can see how much you miss living in the city.

Valentine: Yea, and as for next month, the Canopus constellation shall be glowing and shining; and we'll be wrapping up harvesting.

Nicole: If I were to marry, I'd like to have a night-time wedding in an undisturbed natural area where stars would be visible in a full moon.

Sharon: (Laughs.) Interesting, but I thought you did not want to marry.

Nicole: I would, for you might know the future. Speaking of which; when is the wedding?

Valentine: We are still working on that, preferably in the spring.

Nicole : (*sipping guava juice.)* Why spring?

Valentine: Spring is when nature rebirths, leaves and grass are reborn, and roses soothe; so that would be the perfect time to start our journey as husband and wife.

Nicole: Pretty cool. (*Fascinated.)* So we might expect the wedding in September?

Valentine: Yes. *(In a moment, Ntombi arrives.)*

Ntombi: Good evening, everyone.

Valentine: Hi Ntombi. Take a seat.

Ntombi: Thanks. (She sits.)

Bachelor: Where have you been? We have been waiting for you.

Ntombi: I was busy with some school assignments. I took a metre taxi to come here.

Valentine: Nicole, meet Ntombi; she is an intern in our office.

Nicole: Hi. *(They shake hands.)* I am Nicole, Sharon's sister.

Ntombi: I am Ntombi."

Valentine: She is so brilliant; she is currently doing a Bachelor of Commerce degree at UCT, and she comes three times a week for her internship.

Nicole: That's great. So what about you, Bachelor? Why are you not studying?

Bachelor: I took a gap year to see where I fit before I ventured myself into academia. I have been inducting myself into the Green Winery by doing some shadow work.

Nicole: That's great.

Sharon: Charles, why are you so quiet? We have been talking, and you have not said a word.

Charles: (freighting.) Nothing; I am just thinking...

Sharon: Or scared that your lecturer is here?

Nicole: Please do not be. We are not at False Bay College here.

Charles: *(Calm.)* Cool. I was just in deep thought.

Nicole: Girlfriend stuff?

Charles: *(Laughs.)* Yea, I mean, not really.

Ntombi: How are things between you and Cynthia?

Charles: We are just there; I just couldn't stand her allowing Precious to go on a date with Cas... *(Bachelor deliberately coughs.)*

Bachelor: Ntombi, how are things with you?

Ntombi: They are going?

Sharon: You are also dating?

Valentine: Obviously she is.

Nicole: Where is your boyfriend?

Ntombi: He lives in Hout Bay, he did the same thing as Bachelor, taking a gap year; he's been working at his folks' hotel.

Bachelor: I still cannot understand what you all see in him. He is such a player.

Ntombi: Surely he has changed.

Bachelor: *(Laughs.)* That one I doubt he would. I was just with him today, I cannot believe even shook hands with him.

Charles and Ntombi: What! (Shocked.) You and he shaking hands?

Valentine: *(Curious.)* What's with this guy?

Charles: He and Bachelor are always at each other's throats over a simple misunderstanding. We were all at Fish Hoek High School. They've always been like cats and dogs. Even now, when they meet, it's the same thing?

Sharon: What are they fighting for?

Charles: They are just different characters, I guess. That when we were in high school, he dated like half of the girls, if not two-thirds, and would take even girls Bachelor is zealous about.

Valentine: And what does Bachelor do?

Charles: You know Bachelor, he is more introverted and reserved, can't express himself easily, but is good when given the right platform at the right time.

Ntombi: Yeah, I can attest to that, but then I just hope Casanova has changed.

Bachelor: What do you mean, hope? You are uncertain? I so wish I could understand what makes you all drool at him.

Ntombi: I guess it's because he is a smooth talker, very persuasive, and has such an irresistible countenance.

Bachelor: (rolling eyes.) O please.

Ntombi: Actually, you and him have such a resemblance that it's like you are related—cousins or something.

Valentine: (*Curious.*) Resemblance?

Ntombi: Yea. They have the same eyes, nose, and jawline. Actually, you also look familiar to him.

Valentine: (*The heart pumps harder.*) Who is this guy?

Charles: Casanova.

Valentine: (*anxious.*) I think I must see him.

Bachelor: Let me tell you something that happened today.

Valentine: What happened?

Bachelor: As I was saying, I shook hands with Casanova. I went to the beach, in Fish Hoek, to clear my mind. I bumped into Cynthia, and we spoke; just as we were quietly gazing at the waves, thereafter; Casanova unexpectedly stumbles upon us, then Cynthia leaves. We were then embroiled in conflict as always, arguing. In that moment, a stranger approached us, probably in his 50s, stopped us and told us to shake hands. I felt something, like a magnet; we couldn't stay away from each other. That stranger told us we so resemble each other. He even said, "It's always good to keep an open mind. You never know what life might have in store for you".

Valentine: (*Shutters.*) Hmm. {(*In thought: "O my God, could this be him?" (Could he be the lost twin?)*)}

Nicole: People can resemble each other.

Valentine: I feel like there is more to him. What is his surname?

Bachelor: Smith. Casanova Smith. His mother owns one of the luxurious hotels in Hout Bay.

Valentine: (*Shocked.*) What! (Weeps.)

Sharon: What's wrong, baby?

Valentine: Nothing, nothing, nothing" (*he drinks a glass of water.*)

Sharon: You seem so emotional.

Valentine: Let me get some fresh air. (*He stands and goes.*)

Bachelor: (*Confused.*) Did I say something wrong? (*There is silence at the table.*)

Nicole: Something deep must have touched him. I sense it's something big.

Exeunt

7.3 Act Three

7.3.1 Scene One

(In the morning, at 9:00 a.m., perpendicular Kommetjie Road; whereby the 7th Avenue Lane joins it adjacently on the south; on the north, the Upper De Waal Road is hypotenuse to both lanes, making a 90-degree right angle, which lays the False Bay College. Enter Rose and Casanova.)

Casanova: I still can't believe you slept at Bachelor's house, Rose. What were you thinking?

Rose: What's the big deal, Casanova? I just crashed there because I was too tired to go home."

Casanova: The big deal is that Bachelor and I are just fuel and water, and you know that.

Rose: He may be your enemy, but he's my friend. And he was just being a good host, unlike you. I don't even understand what you two are fighting about.

Casanova: What do you mean by that?

Rose: You kept me waiting for hours in that garage last night, Casanova. You promised you'd be there to pick me up, but you never showed up. I had to call Bachelor to come and get me.

Casanova: I'm sorry Rose, I got caught up with something at work. I didn't mean to keep you waiting.

Rose: Well you did, and it's not the first time either. You always prioritize your work and all the girls you bang over our relationship.

Casanova: That's not true. I care about you Rose- you know that.

Rose: Do I? Because I've heard some rumours that say otherwise.

Casanova: What rumours?

Rose: That you've been seeing Precious behind my back? Is that true?

Casanova: No Rose, I promised you that you were the only one for me. I haven't been seeing anyone else.

Rose: Then why do I keep hearing otherwise? You need to be honest with me, Casanova. I deserve the truth.

Casanova: "I swear to you, Rose." I haven't been seeing anyone else other than Ntombi.

Rose: *(Harshly.)* Stop lying, Casanova! You need to show me you care. And that means being there for me when I need you, not just when it's convenient for you.

Casanova: But then, you got into a relationship with me knowing well that I am dating someone else.

Rose: Precious was not in the picture. Also, do you think having such a good time with you will not attach me to you?

Casanova: What do you mean?

Rose: I am in love with you.

Casanova: But that's not what we agreed upon at first. I thought you understood this.

Rose: Do you really think embracing, kissing, cuddling, going out, hiking, jogging, swimming, and even having wonderful sex will not change someone's feelings and emotions?

Casanova: *(surprised, looking at her.)* I did not know you felt like that. I am sorry. I thought we were just having fun, as we have discussed.

Rose: Well... Now you know. It happens for one to get attached when you are having fun. Don't tell me, *(looking at him)* you can't feel anything between us.

Casanova: I don't know, Rose, I don't know. (He sighs, *brushes his face with his hands, and sighs again.*)

Exeunt

7.3.2 Scene Two

(Green Point in an office, Valentine is sitting at his desk, his brow furrowed as he sifted through stacks of paperwork. Someone tastefully decorated his office with wine bottles and photos of the vineyards that the family owned. As the CEO of the company, he had a lot of responsibilities to take care of. But today, his thoughts were elsewhere.)

Valentine: *(leaning on his chair.)* What if he is the one? I can't just let this go without making more inquiries. Ntombi and Charles spoke about this resemblance between Bachelor and this Casanova, someone I do not know and have not seen before, and Bachelor attested to that with the story of the stranger he met.

(He muttered to himself, his voice low and filled with frustration.)

Valentine: This has been eating away at me ever since that evening on Sunday.

(He leans on the table with his chest, then leans back in the chair with his back; he lets out a deep sigh.)

Valentine: I can't shake the feeling that there is more to the story than what these kids have let on. The way he is being described, his resemblance with Bachelor seems too uncanny to be a coincidence. But then, my suspicions, I can't express them, for Bachelor knows half-truth, and I have never told him that, not only have we lost our parents but his twin also. It is a family secret that only a few trusted relatives are privy to. We kept this a secret because we thought it would devastate Bachelor more.

(As he gazes out the window, lost in thought, Valentine can't help but wonder about the twin brother that Bachelor has never known.)

Valentine: What had happened to him? Could he be still alive? And if he was, where is he now? Could this Casanova be him?

They mentioned that he is a Smith. Smith rings a bell in my mind. If I recall correctly, there was a woman named Smith, who had a partnership with my mother in some hotel in Hout Bay; after that tragedy, she completely cut herself off from us, took everything. *(He pauses, nods, shakes his head, and sighs.)*.

Valentine: No, let me not think too much. I'll end up distressing myself over nothing. Telling Bachelor will only cause chaos and heartache.

(He had a business to run, and his family's livelihood depended on him. But as he returned his attention to the endless stacks of paperwork on his desk, he couldn't help but feel a deep sadness and longing for the truth.)

Valentine: What do I do then? What do I do? *(In a moment, Sharon.)*

Sharon: Good morning, babe. *(She comes towards, then sits on the chair opposite to Valentine.)*

Valentine: Good morning *(smiling.)* Shouldn't you be in court?

Sharon: Don't worry about that. I came to see you. I am sorry I couldn't come yesterday-Monday. How are you?

Valentine: I am fine.

Sharon: *(sighs and gives Valentine a deep stare.)* I mean... how you are? Since Sunday evening, your mood has turned from sweet to sour.

Valentine: Nothing is wrong.

Sharon: I can see right in your eyes that something is bothering you. *(She touches his hand.)* What made you go emotionally when Bachelor's friend mentioned how he resembles some guy from Hout Bay? You can trust me. *(Valentine stands up, goes, and sits on a couch, Sharon follows him.)*

Valentine: This is too heavy. It's a lot to digest.

Sharon: What is it? (*Curious*). Can you tell me why that was such a big deal for you? It seemed like more than just a passing comment.

Valentine: I guess I should explain. Bachelor had a twin brother that got kidnapped when they were infants, when our parents were murdered. It's been a secret for years, and I haven't even told you.

Sharon: What? Bachelor has a twin? Why didn't you tell me this before?

Valentine: I didn't want to upset Bachelor by bringing up painful memories. And to be honest, I do not want to face the possibility that his twin might still be out there somewhere.

Sharon: Oh, my God! That's a huge revelation. Have you talked to Bachelor about this?

Valentine: No, I haven't. I'm not sure how he would react, and I didn't want to raise false hopes if it turned out to be this guy, Casanova.

Sharon: I understand your concerns, but don't you think Bachelor deserves to know the truth?

Valentine: Of course he does. But I need to be sure first. I don't want to raise his hopes or cause him more pain if my suspicions are unfounded.

Sharon: I see. Well, thank you for telling me all of this. It's a lot to process, but I'm glad you trust me enough to confide in me.

Valentine: I trust you completely, Sharon. And I appreciate your understanding of this matter.

Sharon: So what kind of twins were they?

Valentine: They were more like fraternal twins, if I recall.

Sharon: (Sighs.) It must be hard. No wonder you were so attached last evening.

Valentine: Yes. It's been years, and I've learnt to accept that we shall find him no more, but now, I am keen to look for him.

Exeunt

7.3.3 Scene Three

(In the same building, at noon; enter Bachelor and Charles.)

Charles: *(curious.)* So you are telling me you and Casanova shook hands?

Bachelor: Yes, it was so strange. I can't even explain it. We had such a magnet.

Charles: Who knows? You might end up loving each other. I mean good buddies. Truth be told, you have some very similar personality traits, such as the way you smile and the way you show your anger.

Bachelor: Really?

Charles: Yes.

Bachelor: Okay, enough about that guy now. I shall be on TV soon.

Charles: That's wonderful, congratulations. Tell me more.

Bachelor: You know I have been doing some YouTube videos about a variety of topics, so I got noted there. I have been called there to do some speech promotion of sports as the minister of sport and recreation will be there.

Charles: But you don't seem so thrilled?

Bachelor: I am. I just can't believe Marry is conducting this?

Charles: Marry, the teacher?

Bachelor: Yes.

Charles: *(Curious.)* What's wrong with her?

Bachelor: *(avoiding eye contact.)* Nothing, I guess... I guess I am being paranoid since she was my teacher.

Charles: Maybe. Just relax, that one is the coolest educator I know.

Bachelor: Coolest? If only you knew...

Charles: (*Confused.*) What do you mean?

Bachelor: Hey, how are things between you and Cynthia?

Charles: I guess we are fine, we have not called things off.

Bachelor: What do you mean?

Charles: I just couldn't stand her doing that, and she doesn't see how wrong she was.

Bachelor: I don't want you to break up with her because of me, so talk to her, she may have a point.

Charles: Do you think so?

Bachelor: Yes. She wanted nothing that would jeopardise her relationship with you. Maybe it's just the way she handled it.

(*In a moment, Ntombi budges in.*)

Ntombi: Hallo guys.

Both: Hi. How are you?

Ntombi: "I am fine."

Bachelor: Where were you yesterday, you know? I had to cover up for you.

Ntombi: I had a lot on my mind, including this university work.

Bachelor: Trouble in Paradise?

Ntombi: Honestly guys. Can you tell me the truth?

Charles: What truth?

Ntombi: Casanova is cheating on me and has been for a long time. I sense it. (*Bachelor avoids eye contact, then looks back at her.*)

Charles: What makes you say that?

Ntombi: What's the story between him and Precious? I still have some friends from Fish Hoek High School. They tell me stories of how they have been seeing each other and how Casanova has been picking her up from school.

Charles: It is not our place to say that, but you know him. He is not good at all; you should confront him, learn more about it, gather evidence, and proceed from there if you still want to be with him.

(He checks the time.) Guys, I'll see you- I have to go to the CBD to get some stuff.

Bachelor: Cool, I'll see you. *Charles goes.*

Ntombi: Bachelor, I know you. I can even see when you are not telling the truth. Is Casanova cheating on me?

Bachelor: You know him—he's always cheated and manipulated.

Ntombi: Tell me the truth.

Bachelor: Casanova has been dating Rose.

Ntombi: Rose? You mean Max's sister?

Bachelor: Yes. He once stood her up and had to pick her up in a garage some weeks back.

Ntombi: (angrily.) I knew it? And Precious?

Bachelor: I had asked Precious on a date...

Ntombi: What? You asked Precious on a date?

Bachelor: Let me finish...

(Ntombi listens.)

Bachelor:(*continues.*) So what happened was that Cynthia did not like it when Casanova asked her out, but she agreed. She eventually found out that Charles had helped me write a text to her, which escalated the situation, leading to tension between Cynthia and Charles, as Cynthia told Precious. So they have been seeing each other since around Easter. Rose knew that Casanova was dating you, but then she became attached and did not want to let him go.

Ntombi: (*emotional.*) I am shuttered. I am going to kill him.

Bachelor: Please don't, there might be some good in him. I felt something when I shook hands with him.

Ntombi: "I am so angry." I don't care about anything now.

Exeunt

7.3.4 Scene Four

(A hotel on the beach, in Hout Bay; the hotel overlooks the beautiful beach of Hout Bay. The ocean is visible on the front. The leaves of the trees on the hills and mountains far ahead are turning brown and orange. Inside the hotel, a reception desk with a computer and a phone. To the right is a seating area with plush couches and chairs where guests can relax while they wait to check in or out. To the left is a restaurant and bar area, with tables and chairs for guests to enjoy food and drinks while enjoying the ocean view. Behind the reception desk, there's a sign that reads "Helen's Hotel".
Enter a receptionist, Sylvia; is peaking on the phone. Sylvia is just in her mid-20s. Thereafter, Casanova enters.)

Sylvia: Thank you for booking at Helen's Hotel, your room is now readily available for you to check in.

(Listens.)

Sylvia*:* Goodbye thanks.

Casanova: Hello, Sylvia *(smiling and winking.)*

Sylvia: Hey, Casa *(sweet smile.)*

Casanova: You look so beautiful today, your hairstyle is so captivating.

Sylvia: O thanks. *(Touching her hair.)* I didn't even notice.

Casanova: Is mother around?

Sylvia: She is in her office right now.

Casanova: Thanks, I'll go to *her. (he goes and enters the office; suddenly another employee, 20-year-old Pretty, approaches Sylvia.)*

Pretty: *(Curious.)* Is that her son?

Sylvia: Yes. *(Rolling eyes.)*

Pretty: You did not tell me that ma'am has such a handsome son.

Sylvia: Why would I tell you that?

Pretty: (flirting and blushing.) If only I could lay my hands on him.

Pretty: Pretty! Get back to work. You are here to work, not this.

Pretty: Okay, but please Sylvia, introduce me to him. *(She takes some glasses and puts them on a tray.)*

Sylvia: *(laughing, then getting intense.)* I will not do that. Get straight back to work before I report you. *(She leaves, a guess checks in, Casanova is with his mother in an office, Helen, the hotel's owner and manager, is sitting behind the desk.* She's in her mid-50s, well-dressed, and has a friendly smile on her face.)

Casanova: Hey mom.

Helen: Hi, Casanova. How's your stay been so far?

Casanova: It's been great, Mom. I'm really impressed with how well you've managed this hotel. I'm actually thinking of getting into the hotel and accommodation industry myself.

Helen: Oh, really? That's great to hear. I could use some help around here, you know. But have you decided what to study yet?

Casanova: Actually, as I have taken a gap year before deciding, I want to gain some experience and learn more about the industry before committing to a specific course of study.

Helen: That sounds like a good plan.

Casanova: And speaking of learning more about things, have you made any progress in finding out about my real family?

Helen: Casanova, we've been over this before. I told you everything I know, and that's that. You were adopted, and that's all there is to it.

Casanova: But mom, I can't help feeling like there's more to the story. Why won't you tell me who my birth parents are?

Helen: *(sighs.)* Look, Casanova, I know this is important to you, but I just can't bring myself to reveal the truth. I've been keeping a secret from you for all these years, and I fear what might happen if I tell you everything.

Casanova: Scared of what, exactly?

Helen: I don't know, Casanova. I'm just afraid that if I tell you the truth, you'll hate me. And I don't want to lose you.

Casanova: Mom, that's ridiculous. Whatever it is, it can't be worse than not knowing at all. Please, just tell me what you know.

Helen: *(pauses for a moment.)* Alright. But promise me you won't hate me.

Casanova: I promise."

Helen: *(taking a deep breath.)* Your birth parents were both drug addicts. They couldn't take care of you, so they gave you up for adoption. I found out about you through a friend who worked at the adoption agency, and I knew I had to take you in. But something has always scared me. You'd want to leave me once you found out the truth.

Helen: *(pauses for a moment, then hugs his mother.)* Mom, I could never hate you for doing what you thought was best for me. And as for wanting to leave, that will not happen. You're still my mother, no matter what.

Helen*: (tears up.)* Thank you, Casanova. That means a lot to me. And as for your interest in the hotel industry, I am happy to teach you everything I know. You can even take over the hotel someday. Are you enjoying the shadowing work in the hotel?

Casanova: *(smiles.)* Yes, I am. Thanks, Mom. I really appreciate that. And who knows, maybe we can find some long-lost relatives together while we're at it.

Helen: (smiling weakly.) Yeah, I guess. (In a moment, there enters Delilah.)

Delilah: Good day. *(Smiling).*

Helen: (Shocked.) Delilah! What brings you here?

Delilah: (Devilish smile.) Helen, is that how you greet an old friend?

Helen: Hi. (Weary.) How have you been?

Delilah: I am fine. And you must be Casanova? (*He reaches out for his hand.*) You've grown into such a handsome man like your...

Helen: (Interrupting.) Yes, he has. These kids grow so fast these days.

Casanova: (*Delilah gives out his hand to shake.*) I am. *(Seems confused.)*

Delilah: Well, I am a friend of your mother, surely you remember me; last time I saw you; you were in 9th grade.

(Helen is not pleased and is shivering.)

Casanova: Yes, I am. Let me go; maybe you can catch up.

Delilah: Good bye. *(Casanova exit.)* He truly looks like his father.

Helen: (Harshly.) Delilah, what mind games are you playing? Do you know how much I could lose? I would lose everything I have built.

Delilah: Chill... I will say nothing. (She takes a jug of water, and pours it into a glass and drinks, then she takes an apple, throws it up to the ceiling, catches it, and sits down.)

Helen: Delilah, what are you doing? *(She goes and shuts the door, then comes back and stands in front of her.)*

Delilah: I am just here to see an old friend.

Helen: What do you want? I know you. You are not here to catch up with me.

Delilah: How do you think you are going to keep this secret?

Helen: You know this can never come out.

Delilah: Let me see... (she *pauses, looks up at the ceiling, then stares at Helen.)* Imagine if Valentine Green were to find out that all this time, you have kidnapped Bachelor's twin.

Helen: I did not kidnap him. I took him from the centre; only to find later that he is a son of Richard Green.

Delilah: Not only that, a son of your partner, Bridget. How would that look? Will they not see you as the murderer of Richard and Bridget while their babies were a few months old?

Helen: You know I had nothing to do with that.

Delilah: It is not about whether you did it or not, it is about how it would look. You took the hotel for yourself, and even removed Bridget's name while you were partners. Think not only about how Valentine and Bachelor would feel, but how "your son" would feel.

Helen: *(Shivering.)* God forbid! You are aware that under the law, if one of the partners dies, the partnership dissolves.

Delilah: Do not use the Lord's name in vain. Please leave God out of this. Sit, you must be tired. *(Helen sits, drinks some water.)*

Helen: What do you want, Delilah? You want money?

Delilah: I do not want your money. I have got bigger plans than you giving me peanuts.

Helen: Name your prize.

Delilah: I don't want it; I told you I was here to catch up with an old friend.

Helen: (Angrily.) And this is your way of catching up?

Delilah: Okay, Helen. You got me. Valentine is getting married.

Helen: *(Surprised.)* Really? That's great.

Delilah: I can't believe you are saying "that's great." That wedding must not happen.

Helen: And how am I going to do that? I don't even know his fiancé.

Delilah: Sharon. Sharon is the sister of Nicole, who is friends with my daughter Leah. Leah wants Valentine. They were once together before he went back to Sharon. Oh, if only my daughter had listened. We would be worth millions now.

Helen: Are you planning to use your daughter to get rich?

Delilah: Remember, that Richard Green would have been my husband, had Bridget not taken him from me. So now Valentine, his son, must marry my daughter Leah. And this is where you come in.

Helen: How?

Delilah: You will arrange a room for Valentine and Leah to meet here. Make it believable that Valentine is cheating on Sharon. It shall break her heart, and my daughter shall have him.

Helen: You are crazy? How can I do that?

Delilah: Do not worry. I shall send details on how we shall plot this.

(Helen is shuttered, pale, and reddish; thereafter, Casanova is sitting alone on a couch at the reception, busy with his Nokia Express Music cell phone on Facebook; the music plays loudly.)

Pretty: Hi.

Casanova: *(She seems to be not hearing her.)*

Pretty: (Aloud.) Hey!

Casanova: Hey. Sorry, I wasn't hearing you.

Pretty: Can you please lower down the music? It's too loud, and some guests have sent me to tell you.

Casanova: I am so sorry. *(Switches it off.)* I'll just put on my headsets.

Pretty: I am Pretty.

Casanova: I can see that. *(Smiling.)*

Pretty: I mean, my name is Pretty. *(She points at her name tag on the left side of her chest.)*

Casanova: O, I am sorry. I just have a lot on my mind. I am Casanova. Casanova Smith.

Pretty: Are you checking in? Can I assist you? *(Blushing, Sylvia far ahead notices her.)*

Casanova: No, not at all. I was just here to see my mother. *(Pointing to the office.)* She must be busy with a friend now.

Pretty: She's your mother?

Casanova: Yes.

Pretty: You have a lovely mother. *(Deep smile.)*

Casanova: Thank you. *(Pretty fixes her dress. Sylvia is looking at her astounded, opening her eyes and mouth wide.)*

Pretty: You came to visit her? *(Sylvia calls her.)* I am coming. *(She picks up some empty bottle juice on the table). Let me get this for you. (She goes to Sylvia.)*

(Far off.)

Sylvia: Pretty, what are you doing?

Pretty: What did I do?

Sylvia: Stay away from Casanova if you know what's good for you. This is so unprofessional and unethical.

Pretty: I did nothing.

Sylvia: I saw you blushing and flirting with him. He is your boss' son. Stay away from him. He also has a girlfriend.

Pretty: *(Disappointed.)* He has a girlfriend?

Sylvia: You see? *(Pointing at her, opening eyes wide).* Don't even crush him. *(Suddenly Ntombi arrives, seems bitter, and approaches Casanova.)*

Pretty: (Curious). Is that the girlfriend?

Sylvia: Yes. *(Whispering.)*

Pretty: She seems bitter, looks like trouble in paradise.

Sylvia: (Whispering.) Yes, very possible. Casanova is a Casanova, womaniser and player.

Pretty: *(putting a tray on the desk.)* Are you serious?

Sylvia: Yes. He comes here with different girls, bangs them. He has a special room for them, room 268. It is up there at the top, and it is no longer even booked, for he has reserved it for himself to do this.

Pretty: Wow. *(Clapping hands, looks at them, then looks at Sylvia.)* So, have you been in room 268 as well?

Sylvia: (Felling guilty.) What do you mean?

Pretty: I mean... have you also been in room 268?

Sylvia: "Pretty, get back to work."

Pretty: (*opens her mouth and touches it.*) You have been in room 268!

Sylvia: (*Harshly.*) Get back to work Pretty. Leave me alone.

Pretty: I can't believe it. (*Pretty goes, then Casanova and Ntombi are on the couch arguing, Sylvia is looking far off.*)

Casanova: Can we just go upstairs? There are too many people there.

Ntombi: No, I am not going there. I have been there, only to know I am not the only one. Me, Rose, Precious, who else? Tell me!

Casanova: I can't believe you listen to all the trash that guy told you.

Ntombi: Is he lying? Casanova, you are up to no good. I can't believe you betrayed me like this. Ruth confirmed this to me as well. You cheated on me, made me think you had changed, but you are still the same. I can't look at you right now. I am so angry. And Precious, of all people, how could she do this to me? I am going to kill her.

Casanova: Ntombi, please don't go confront Precious."

Ntombi: Why not? She is treacherous, and she must know she is not the only one. As for you, I am so angry; I am so disappointed in you. I do not even want to talk with you right now.

Casanova: I am sorry.

Ntombi: Are you sorry that you got caught, or are you sorry about that because you are genuinely sorry?

Casanova: Let me fix this.

Ntombi: Fix what? Fix what? What the hell are you going to fix? This is unfixable. (*Sylvia comes, to calm them.*)

Sylvia: (*in a low, harsh voice.*) Guys, stop this. This is a business. Take your fight somewhere else. Ntombi, go for now, or take

Casanova somewhere else. People are watching you right now. You do not want ma'am to come here and address this herself.

Ntombi: We are not done here. (*She goes.*)

Casanova: Ntombi, wait... (*He tries to reach her, but Sylvia grabs him.*)

Sylvia: Let her calm down first, then speak to her. Right now, she can't stand you, and you chasing her; will just add fuel to the fire. You need to calm down, clear your head, and think thoroughly about what you really want. You do not want to make hasty decisions that you shall regret later, then repeat the same mistake.

Casanova: I guess you are right. (*Calm.*)

Sylvia: (*Whispering*). Come, I have got something to cool you down at the bar. (Calling Pretty.) Pretty1 Pretty! (*Pretty turns around.*) Go stand up for me at the reception, I will be back just now. (*Pretty is puzzled and dissatisfied.*) Go! (*Pretty goes.*) I want you to tell me what has happened.

Casanova: I knew it. What are you going to do?

Sylvia: Maybe I can help you, advise you on what you can do, but in the end, it shall be your choice.

Exeunt

7.3.5 Scene Five

(In the afternoon, at Fish Hoek High School, Andrews is preparing to go home, packing his files and books.)

Andrews: Hey *(Looking at his wife's photos.)* I miss you. I really miss you. *(Marry enters.)*

Marry: Hi. *(Smiling.)*

Andrews: *(Frighten).* Hey... I did not expect to see you. *(They march close to each other and embrace.)* I really, enjoy your company.

Marry: Me too. *(Sighs on Andrews' chest.)* You are so sweet. *(They look at each other and kiss.)*

Andrews: You are so lovely. *(He is kissing her, then suddenly, over the window, Cynthia comes and catches them.)*

Cynthia: *(outside, shocked.)* Wow! I have now witnessed this with my own eyes. I had to confront him. Now this! What should I do? Budge in and let them see I have caught them? I can't drag Precious into this, since she is still a student here. That's why I said I must come alone. Andrews must stop this! I am going in. *(She budges in, in an instance, Andrews's and Marry break away, shocked, and shivering.)*

Andrews' and Marry: Cynthia! *(She is shuddering and shivering.)*

Cynthia: Apologies. I was looking for Charles, and he had said I would get him here.

Andrews: But this is a school. Why would he say that? And he is no longer a student here, but at False Bay College.

Cynthia: "I saw everything." You do not have to pretend like nothing happened.

Marry: I am so sorry; please say nothing to anyone, especially Charles. (*She takes her bag and goes.*)

Cynthia: Mr. Andrews, how can you do this?

Andrews: (*shivering and stuttering.*) I am so sorry. I did not mean any of this.

Cynthia: It is not me, you are going to have to apologise to, but your son, Charles!

Andrews: No, no, please do not tell Charles.

Cynthia: "I will not tell him. You are going to tell him, and your wife as well.

Andrews: No, this is my life, my marriage. I do not want to lose my family.

Cynthia: (*yelling.*) You should have thought about that before immersed in infidelity. Also; how sure am I this affair will not continue as you will get away with your infidelity with no consequences?

Andrews: I think as of now, things between me and Marry are over.

Cynthia: You think? You think so, Mr. Andrews?

Andrews: No, I know it is. How can we continue when we have been caught?

Cynthia: But then you have to tell Charles or confess to your wife. Do you know how worried Charles has been about you two? That you are so disconnected has been bothering him.

Andrews: I didn't realise. Having this affair must have swayed my mind away from my priorities and the ones that I love.

Cynthia: Now, you know. Act quickly before things get out of hand. I had come here to confront you about this, and then I witnessed it with my own eyes.

Andrews: (*surprised.*) You knew about this?

Cynthia: Yes. And I know what I am doing is not right. You are old enough to be my father, and I am dating your son. But then, people have been watching, right?

Andrews: *(Curious).* What do you mean?

Cynthia: Precious and Casanova caught you in a restaurant, then Precious told me; thereafter, I was having a soliloquy; Bachelor overhead.

Andrews: *(Shocked.)* What! So they all know about this?

Cynthia: Make sure this does not get to Charles before you tell him, otherwise, hell shall break loose.

Andrews: You are so brave, very bold, Cynthia. I am shuttered; I am defeated.

Exeunt

7.3.6 Scene Six

(Kirstenbosch National Botanical Garden: a warm glow of light spills onto the stage, illuminating a breath-taking scene. It is late afternoon, the sun is casting long shadows across the landscape; the sky is a warm orange hue, with the sun halfway to setting, signalling the approach of evening; enter Bachelor and Ndalo.)

Ndalo: Do you see how adorable this scenery is? The garden is an explosion of colour and texture, with a variety of plant species dotting the landscape. From the towering trees, with their majestic branches stretching towards the sky, to the lush green grass carpeting the ground, this botanical garden is truly a feast for the senses.

Bachelor: Yea, I can see; look at the state of roses far across, standing tall and proud; with their deep red petals bathed in the soft, golden light of the sun. *(As the breeze gently blows, the flowers sway in unison, creating a mesmerising dance of colour and movement.)*

Ndalo: This botanical garden is home to a variety of other flowers, each with their own unique beauty. *(Some bloom in vivid shades of purple, others in soft pinks and pastels, while others boast bright yellows and oranges that seem to light up across.)*

Bachelor: Ndalo, you are so immersed in nature that I always knew you'd be a florist, or botanist; hence, you are studying botany.

Ndalo: Yes, just hear the sound of flowing waters filling the air, with streams and waterfalls meandering their way through the garden. *(They can see the reflection of the trees and flowers shimmering on the surface of the water, creating a dreamlike atmosphere.)*

Bachelor: *(They are walking.)* Coming here, I have always adored to gaze upon the glittering bridges made from wood, heading deeper into the botanical garden, where I can explore countless treasures hidden within. *(As the autumn breeze begins to blow, the leaves on the trees have turned into vibrant shades of red, orange, and yellow.)*

Ndalo: I am captured by these shades of yellow, orange, and red of the leaves, which add another layer of beauty to an already stunning scene. Just look at how many people are taking in the sights and sounds of the Kirstenbosch National Botanical Garden this afternoon, gazing across with a sense of wonder and awe at the majestic nature.

Bachelor: Yes, indeed, this is one of the places I come to to clear my mind.

Ndalo: What's going on?

Bachelor: Nothing.

Ndalo: Bachelor, I know what's going on. *(He pauses, they stand still on a wooden bridge.)*

Bachelor: *(sighs, looks at the trees and birds flying across, and then stares at Ndalo.)* What is going on?

Ndalo: You meddle in other people's affairs and do not focus on yourself.

Bachelor: I take that as an offence. What have I done?

Ndalo: You mean you do not know? You deliberately sabotaged Casanova's relationship with Rose and Ntombi, let alone what you tried with Precious.

Bachelor: I do not think this is any of your business; Casanova needs to change.

Ndalo: And he must change on your terms? Why can't you let him live his own life, the way he wants to?

Bachelor: Do you realise how many people he has hurt? On top of it, it's his girlfriends that come to me seeking some advice and raising their suspicions that they are being cheated upon. What must I do? Say that he is an angel?

Ndalo: Can't you allow him to explore himself?

Bachelor: Explore himself by being such a fuck boy? That guy needs to change, I know he can, he just needs someone to bring some sense in his head.

Ndalo: And when will you change?

Bachelor: Do I need to change?

Ndalo: Yea, get some relationships and leave other people alone."

Bachelor: I know, you want to back up your friend, but I can't believe you justify his actions like that. Why are you so drawn to him?

Ndalo: No, I am not, Why can't you respect him as well?

Bachelor: Respect him? That guy deserves no respect, he is disrespectful to himself.

Ndalo: No, if you've ever been in a relationship, you'd understand what guys do. Nothing serious.

Bachelor: That is one of the most sexist, patriarchal, and heteronormative ideals and statements ever; toying with girls doesn't make you a better person, nor does it show your manhood. It just shows how foolish you are and how archaic your mind is.

Ndalo: You really can't stand him, just as he cannot stand you; you hate his guts.

Bachelor: Yea... mean... no! It's not a matter of whether I can stand him or not; it's a matter of his actions, which are unacceptable. Casanova is manipulative, explosive, and untrustworthy; he is good looking outside but bad looking outside; curse me if I am wrong and bless me if I am right. But all in all, I believe there is a good soul there, deep in a comma, it just needs to be triggered so he can be a better person.

Ndalo: And how do you know that?

Bachelor: It happened some weeks ago, that we shook hands, and I felt something. I could sense a change in his heart and eyes.

Ndalo: You and he shook hands, he never told me that.

Bachelor: He does not have to tell you everything. You know, let's just leave this topic before it escalates into a situation beyond repair. Let's just speak about nature and tell more about the invasive and indigenous floral species in this area.

Ndalo: "Okay, cool." *(They walk.)*

Exeunt

7.3.7 Scene Seven

(Fish Hoek, the sky is partly cloudy, clouds are scattered across, the sunlight is deemed, with orange raises, wind blowing with a cooling breeze from the sea, yellowish, reddish leaves blown across the atmosphere; enter Joshua and Valentine.)

Valentine: Are you enjoying your retirement so far, uncle?

Joshua: Yes, son. I am, and what makes me happier is to see you grow up to be the man your father and my brother wished for.

Valentine: Thanks a lot. I am so grateful for all that you have done for me and Bachelor.

Joshua: (emotional.) You do not have to; it was my mandate. But thank you, appreciate it.

Valentine: How old are you now, Uncle?

Joshua: I am 63, your father would have been 65 this year, had not that tragedy happened.

Valentine: *(eyes filling with tears.)* What I hate the most is that justice was never done, and I still do not believe those two men orchestrated that themselves only.

Joshua: "Valentine, we have been through this."

Valentine: I know I know. There is something I want to ask you. It's been bothering me.

Joshua: About what?

Valentine: Bachelor's twin.

Joshua: We have spoken many times about this. I just can't handle it any more.

Valentine: Uncle, I believe we have a chance to get Matthew back.

Joshua: What do you mean?

Valentine: Okay, there is this guy, whom I have recently heard about but have never seen, who is called Casanova. He went to Fish Hoek High School with him. They all state how much they resemble each other, and even a stranger confirmed it, when it saw them arguing at the beach.

Joshua: Really?

Valentine: Yes. What puzzles me, is hearing that he is a Smith. Do you remember anyone named Smith at that time? There is something I recall. Wasn't mother in partnership in a hotel with some Smith woman?

Joshua: Yes, she was. I saw them many times at that time when Bridget and Richard were still alive. But what I know about her is that she was barren. She ended up adopting a child in one of the orphanages a year or so after your parents died. Thereafter, we slowly disconnected until today. I saw her a few times over the years, but I haven't seen her for the past ten years now.

Valentine: What was her name?

Joshua: Helen. Helen Smith. Also, there was a woman who worked in the very same orphanage centre, by name of Delilah, she was a friend of hers. I don't know if they are still friends.

Valentine: What can you tell me more about her?

Joshua: I met her back in 2007, he had a house in Simon's Town and a daughter by name of Leah.

Valentine: *(shocked.)* What!

Joshua: Do you know her?

Valentine: No. It's just that the name Leah sounds familiar. Thank you, uncle, for this information. Where is David?

Joshua: He is busy with the suppliers now since it's time for harvesting, I just got a 100% nectar juice from him yesterday. He is in Stellenbosch, managing his company.

Valentine: I tried to look for him even on social media, but nothing, and he changes his cell phone numbers so often.

Joshua: Go to that diary and check it, I think I have written it there.

Valentine: Thanks. (*He goes, opens the diary, and then shoots it with his Apple iPhone.*). Uncle, thanks for the information and desert. Let me go, it is dusk now, and it's such a long drive home.

Joshua: Thanks for the visit. (*He stands up and embraces him.*)

Exeunt

7.3.8 Scene Eight

(Fish Hoek, at twilight: the sky is painted in a reddish-orange, it is a bit cold, the clouds are partially spread across the heavens, and stars are slowly appearing, streets, wind blowing with a cooling breeze from the sea, yellowish, reddish leaves are blown across the atmosphere; lights are lighting. Enter Precious in a restaurant, sitting in a veranda, She is busy texting on her cell phone, when suddenly, Rose appears from inside, She approaches her).

Rose: You! (Intense face.)

Precious: (Confused.) And then?

Rose: What do you think you are doing, Precious?

Precious: What are you talking about?

Rose: (sitting). You know exactly what I am talking about.

Precious: (Puzzled). What?

Rose: Precious, what the hell do you think you're doing dating Casanova?

Precious: Excuse me? I'm not sure what you're talking about.

Rose: Don't play dumb with me, girl. Bachelor told me that Casanova took you out on a date.

Precious: Okay, yes, he did. But I don't see what that has to do with you.

Rose: Are you serious, right now? Casanova is my man, and you know that!

Precious: First of all, Casanova is not your man. He's a player who's been seeing both of us. And secondly, I didn't know he was dating you when he asked me out.

Rose: You expect me to believe that? You knew damn well that he was seeing other women.

Precious: Look, I'm sorry if I hurt you, but I'm not going to apologize for going out with someone who asked me on a date. And besides, you knew what kind of guy Casanova was.

Rose: "I may have known that he was a player. But I didn't expect him to stoop so low as to go out with my friend!"

Precious: Your friend? We barely know each other, Rose. And you can't blame me for your man's actions. If you have a problem with Casanova, take it up with him.

Rose: You're damn right; I will. But I also have a problem with you, Precious. You knew that Casanova was seeing me, and yet you still went out with him. That's messed up.

Precious: I didn't know, Rose. And even if I had, I wouldn't have cared. I'm not going to let someone dictate who I can and can't date.

Rose: Fine, do what you want. But don't expect me to just sit back and watch while you try to steal my man.

Precious: I'm not trying to steal your man, Rose. And he's not even worth fighting over. Trust me, I've learnt that the hard way.

Rose: Whatever. I don't want to talk to you right now. Just stay away from Casanova, okay?

Precious: You don't have to worry about that. I'm done with him. Moreover, what you are doing is so lame, you are devaluing yourself. You are fighting me instead of the man who fooled both of us. You are already in college, but you are fighting with a high school girl over a man, and you do not even know he loves you. Does he even love you?

Rose: That is none of your business! Stay away from him.

Precious: Wow. I am not surprised, you must have never been loved. I pity you. Let Casanova be the one, fighting for you and not you fighting for him. It's better if it's a man who deeply loves a woman than if it's a woman loving a man so deeply. As for myself, I will confront Casanova and take it from there, I am not going to do what you are doing, acting so low. *(She stands up, finishes a coffee.)* Let me go. Goodbye, I do not have time for trash. (She goes.)

Rose: *(She is left shuttered and angry.)* Who the hell does she think she is?

Exit

7.3.9 Scene Nine

(The following day. Enter Cynthia and Charles, at noon, at False Bay College, in the lecture room, with the other students sitting by, awaiting a lecturer.)

Cynthia: I really hate that guy; I can't stand him!

Charles: Now, you hate him, don't you? Did I not tell you that he is up to no good?

Cynthia: Don't tell me I told you so. I did not tell Precious that he had to date Casanova with a gun pointed on her face. All I said, was that he can't date my boyfriend's, for my own valid reasons.

Charles: I get your point, but you just let her into the vulture. Now she has to go through such trauma.

Cynthia: Precious is old enough, to fight for herself; she said I must allow her to make her own decisions, and I have. It's not my fault that Casanova cheated on her with Rose and Ntombi. I can't believe you kept that from me.

Charles: As if you have not kept something from me? *(Looking at her.)*

Cynthia: *(feeling guilty.)* No, there isn't anything I am keeping from you. *(Avoiding eye contact.)*

Charles: I did not say there is... *(Notices how she is turning eyes away from him.)* Or... is there something you are keeping from me?

Cynthia: No, there isn't. (Looking forward, Nicole; the lecturer comes in.)

Nicole: Good afternoon, everyone.

Cynthia: Let's pay attention to the lecturer. I am just glad we have fixed things.

Exeunt

171

7.3.10 Scene Ten

(Hout Bay, Helen's Hotel, Enter Casanova, and Ndalo.)

Ndalo: You are truly in a dilemma, buddy. Uphakathi kweBhayi neTinarha!

Casanova: Yes, Ndalo. And now, Rose is telling me that she is now so deeply in love with me. I had thought we understood each other.

Ndalo: And how do you feel?

Casanova: I don't know, man, I don't know, I have never thought that way for her.

Ndalo: Bachelor truly ruined your fun.

Casanova: He has indeed. I had a headache even though we are now cool, after that incident at the beach.

Ndalo: He told me about it. I think he was just pretending. That guy hates your guts. You could have heard all the bad things he said about you.

Ndalo: What did he say?

Ndalo: How vile and selfish you are, that you can never be trusted and need to be shunned.

Casanova: (Pondering.) Really? It's unlike him, we may dispute that, but he isn't a cold-hearted person.

Ndalo: He has told all your girlfriends what a bad person you are, and you are now going to lose all of them because of him. He even said your mind is so archaic and full of yourself.

Casanova: I didn't realise he hates me that much.

Ndalo: He surely does. (In an instance, he notices Precious approaching.) Look, she really looks inflamed.

(Far off Sylvia and Pretty whispering.)

Sylvia: Just wait and see, hell is about to break loose.

Pretty: (Curious.) Is that one of his girlfriend's approaching?

Sylvia: Yes, she is from Fish Hoek. I can't believe she came all the way from there to here. Just watch.

Ndalo: Hey Precious, I have not seen you in a long time. How are you?

Precious: I am fine. I want to speak to him.

Ndalo: Okay, let me give you some space. (*He goes.*)

Casanova: Hi. (*He hugs her, but Precious isn't thrilled, they sit on the couch.*) What's wrong?

Precious: Are you seriously going to ask me that? You do not know what is going on?

Casanova: I don't know.

Precious*: (angrily.)* I am tired of your lies. To be confronted by your side chicks like that, really pissed me off.

Casanova: What are you talking about?

Precious: Do not play your mind games with me. Rose confronted me yesterday evening at dusk. She bumped into me in a restaurant, and he had the guts to tell me I must stay away from you because you are her man.

(Far off: Sylvia and Pretty.)

Sylvia: Go listen, pretend you are cleaning a table or picking up some rubbish.

Pretty: Okay. (*She goes.*)

(*Casanova and Precious are arguing.*)

Casanova: That was so low for her. She shouldn't have done that. She knows I do not love her, have never been in love with her.

Precious: She knows? What do you mean? What have you been doing with her?

Casanova: Before I met you, I had been involved with her, and it was just for fun; we both acknowledged that. It's not my fault she got emotionally attached.

Precious: Not your fault? Not your fault? (They notice Pretty, then continue talking.) What do you think was going to happen?

Casanova: I did not mean any of this. I am sorry.

Precious: What about Ntombi? Bachelor has revealed all your dirt.

Casanova: So you listen to Bachelor over me? That guy has never liked me; he is my obstacle in everything.

Precious: Stop blaming Bachelor for your actions. You are the one at fault. (*While cleaning the table, Pretty is staring at them.*)

Casanova: (To Pretty.) What are you looking at? Can you finish up, please? Make haste!

Pretty :(Frighten.) I am, I am done... sorry. (She picks up an empty bottle and goes.)

Casanova: Precious, I love and adore you."

Precious: No, you do not. You are not even regretful for what you have done.

Casanova: I am. I am sorry for all that has happened. (In a moment, Ntombi arrives, she notices them and frowns.)

(Far off; Sylvia and Pretty.)

Pretty: It is a film.

Sylvia: Just watch; I hope this shall not escalate, for lady boss shall be pissed.

Ntombi: Yes! Now I have confirmed it. So you two are an item. How dare you, Precious, how can you do this to me.

(*Casanova is frustrated, he does not know what to do, he is mumbling.*)

Precious: I did not know he was dating you. (Ntombi, takes a glass of water and pours it on Precious.)

Casanova: Ntombi no. How can you do this?

Ntombi: You are a liar and cheater, as you have always been. I trusted you, you betrayed me, you fool!

(Far off)

Sylvia: (shocked.) I did not realise this girl has such drama!

Pretty: I hope it doesn't turn into a fight.

Casanova: Guys, listen, Let's go into a more private place and talk well.

Both: "Hell no!"

Precious: And you, Ntombi, look how you ruined my outfit, you slacker! (Yelling).

Ntombi: Ubiza bani ngononkiloyi?

(*She slaps her, Precious is shocked, she tries to fight back, and Casanova gets between them.*)

Casanova: Ladies, please. (They all start yelling at each other, causing a scene, Helen comes out.)

Helen: What the hell is going on here? Sylvia! (Sylvia, runs to them.) Who the hell are you?

Ntombi: Ask your son.

Helen: Casanova, what is going on?

Casanova: Mother! I am sorry!

Helen: Get them out of here, Sylvia, take them out. This is a business, not a circus. And you, Casanova, you better have a solid explanation. How dare you bring your girlfriends to fight in my hotel?

Precious: I am done here, we are through.

Ntombi: You are a bustard, Casanova!

Helen: Terri a little. Don't belittle my son, like that in my premises! Throw them out! (Casanova goes with them, along with Sylvia.)

Sylvia: Out! This way, guys! (*As they go, Valentine enters; he bumps into Casanova, they look at each other, Casanova continues, Valentine stares at him until they are outside.*)

Valentine: (Turning into Helen, Helen is shocked and stunned.) Good day, Miss.

Helen: *(Shivering.)* Hi. It's been years.

Valentine: It has indeed been. (*Sylvia, comes back, goes to the reception, Pretty cleans up the table, then goes to Sylvia.*)

Pretty: Who is that? (pointing at Valentine.)

Sylvia: I don't know; I have never seen him.

Pretty: Helen's face went pale and red. It's like she had seen a ghost.

Sylvia: "I wonder."

Pretty: But look at him. Isn't he the eldest son? He looks like Casanova.

Sylvia: I doubt Helen has any other children besides Casanova. Unless she has been hiding it for all these years. That woman is so secretive.

(On the couch.)

Helen: How have you been?

Valentine: I am doing pretty well.

Helen: What brings you here? Is the company running well? I heard you took over.

Valentine: Very well. I'd say things are pretty good.

Helen: Well, that is great. You have grown and resemble your father much. He may rest in peace.

Valentine: Thanks.

Helen: Any woman in your life? Bridgett truly wanted you to get married and have a supportive partner so you could be an example to your younger brother.

Valentine: There is, I am actually engaged to Sharon. She is so amazing and supportive.

Helen :(*Weak smile.*) So what brings you here?

Valentine: I wanted to speak to you about something. Reading any information, you may have, about Bachelor's twin.

Helen: (*shivering with fear.*) What! Can we go to my office, please!

Valentine: Yes. (*They stand up and go.*)

Pretty: Have you noticed? It's like she is not herself. Helen always has that loving smile, but that one, isn't that pleasing.

Sylvia: Yes, Pretty; I can tell something is going on there. But you can never know with Helen. She is full of surprises. She doesn't usually bring people into her office unless it's something really deep or an important business deal, but I doubt this man is here for business; he is not even carrying a briefcase.

(Inside Helen's office.)

Helen: Can I get you some nectar or guava juice?

Valentine: No thanks, I have just had one. Just some water, please. (She gives him still water inside a bottle.)

Helen: *(sitting on the couch):* How can I help you?

Valentine: I wanted to know, if you knew any woman by the name of Delilah, who once worked in an orphanage centre. Perhaps she can help me get a hold of Matthew, Bachelor's twin.

Helen: (Anxious.) I wish, could, I have never heard that name. Why asking this now?

Valentine: I have been thinking, that maybe; he might still be alive. I feel like we did not try enough to find him.

Helen: Your younger brother had a twin?

Valentine: Yes, surely you remember. Don't you recall when you came when they were just infants?

Helen: (feeling guilty.) Yea, I may recall.

Valentine: If you have any information that may help?

Helen: What information? It's been years since 1992, apartheid had just even dismantled in 1990, we had not yet even had a democratic election.

Valentine: Any orphanage centre you may know which was in existence at that time?

Helen: Not that I know of, the thing there is plenty not just one, so I may not be certain. If may ask, what happened to him?

Valentine: He was abducted in that exact same night, luckily Bachelor was me in the bathroom. Those thugs admitted to have abandoned him in an orphanage, but we have no trace of such.

Helen: I am so sorry. I wish I could help, but I absolutely no information.

Valentine: You don't know any Delilah-named woman who worked in one of the centres around?

Helen: (*shocked and shivering.*) No. Not at all. Where did you get that name?

Valentine: My uncle mentioned someone who may have worked there around that time.

Helen: I wish I could. But I'll try to dig up some information, and if I find anything, I'll alert you.

Valentine: Thank you. I'd appreciate. Let me go now. I'll keep in touch. (*They stand up, Helen walks him out, and then Helen comes back and dials a cell.*)

Helen: (on the line): Delilah, we need to speak. (Delilah is on the line.) No, do not come here, I will come to you there in Simon's Town.

Exit

7.3.11 Scene Eleven

(Fish Hoek High School, is in the afternoon, the school is about to close, learners are roaming around, enter Andrews in his classroom.)

Andrews: Learners, for your homework; go search and read on Balance Sheet, its format and layout. Tomorrow we shall discuss it, and a have a small assessment.

(Learners Afar)

1ˢᵗ Learner: He has been cheating on his wife all this time.

2ⁿᵈ Learner: (Shocked.) How did you get that?

1ˢᵗ Learner: I heard from Ruth, apparently Precious sported them while he was on a date with Casanova.

Ruth: (Turning back.) Guys, don't do this. And you, (frowning.)—I instructed you not to say a word, but you are now blabbing it to the entire school. How will Precious trust me next time?

3ʳᵈ Learner: Stop making yourself a saint. You have been taking gossip out of this school to UCT, telling Ntombi about Precious.

2nd Learner: Why didn't Precious come to school?

Ruth: She bunked it. She gave me her uniform, then she wore some casual clothes so she could go and face Casanova in Hout Bay about his cheating saga. *(They laugh).*

3ʳᵈ Learner: She really has guts!

Andrews: (Notices some learners are not paying attention.) Hey, Ruth, and your friends there... Can you tell us what you're all giggly about?

Ruth: (*looking forward.*) Nothing Sir. (*Frighten.*)

Andrews: It does not look like nothing. (*There is silence. The bell rings.*) Stop talking when I am teaching. It's irritating and disturbing. You are all excused. (*Leaners go, then Marry enters.*)

Andrews: (*Surprised.*) Marry! What are you doing here, I thought we have been through this.

Marry: We haven't seen each other since yesterday. What are we going to do?

Andrews: Let's call it an end; it is even worse now that we have been caught.

Marry: By who? Did Cynthia notice anything?

Andrews: She knows. She even confronted me, she saw us. Now she wants me to confess. I can't do that; I don't want to lose my marriage.

Marry: What about me? Have you not said you love me?

Andrews: Stop confusing pleasure with love. Yes, I did enjoy being with you, but now I cannot continue. What if my son finds out about this? Worse yet, he has been noticing how distant we have become with his mother.

(*Ruth and leaners outside.*)

Ruth: Things look so tense.

1st Leaner: Do you think his son might have found out?

Ruth: I don't think so. I doubt Cynthia and Precious would tell him.

2nd Learner: Then find out for us.

3rd Learner: Yes.

Ruth: No guys, I do not want to get into trouble. (*Andrews comes towards the door.*)

Andrews: Can you just leave? Go home now, you said you were tired and wanted to go home. (*They go, and Andrews closes the door.*)

Marry: You have a point there; I am terrified. But surely we can still do something.

Andrews: No, we cannot! I even told you that my wife would be arriving shortly. In all, we are done. I can't continue anymore.

Marry: After all this time. You rode me like a horse, and now you spit on me like saliva?

Andrews: Can you not see what is at stake here? My marriage and my son! When we started this, we told ourselves that there were no strings attached.

Marry: But you can't control how your heart feels.

Andrews: How the heart feels? How can you entangle your heart with another man's wife? It's not my fault that you got attached.

Marry: *(angry, and slapping him.)* You basted! You men are all the same. You use women for your pleasure when it is convenient for you, moreover, when things go bad, you throw them away like rubbish.

Andrews: I am sorry. *(Trying to ease her and touch her.)*

Marry: No, don't touch me. Go to your wife, and don't come back to me in the winter when your wife is away. *(She goes.)*

Andrews: *(Andrews sits alone at his desk, staring blankly at the wall. He takes a deep breath and begins to speak to himself).*

(Frustrated): What have I done? How could I have been so foolish? I betrayed the woman I love, my loyal wife, for a fling with a colleague. What was I thinking?

I thought I could handle it. It was just a little bit of fun. But now, everything is falling apart. Cynthia knows about us, and I can't face her. I can't even look my son in the eye anymore. I'm a hypocrite. I teach my students about honesty and integrity, yet here I am, living a lie.

I know what I need to do. I need to confess to my wife. I need to face the consequences of my actions. But I'm scared. I'm scared of losing her, of losing my family, and losing everything I hold dear.

(Sighs.) :And then there's Marry. I thought I could end things amicably, but she's become attached to me. She slapped me when I told her it was over. I don't blame her for being angry. I'm just another man who used her for his own selfish desires. It's true, all men are the same. We use women and then discard them when we're done.

(Inflicted.) :I hate myself for what I've done. I hate that I've hurt the people I care about the most. I hate that I've betrayed their trust. But most of all, I hate that I can't take it back. I can't undo what I've done. I'm stuck with this guilt and shame for the rest of my life.

(Pondering.) I don't know if I'll ever be able to forgive myself. All I can do now is try to make things right, to be a better man, a better husband, and a better father. I just hope it's not too late.

7.3.12 Scene Twelve

(It is middle autumn, and the sky is filled with gloomy clouds that hang low over the Atlantic Ocean. The wind is blowing briskly, causing the waves to crash against the rocky shore with a thunderous roar. The sun, half-way to setting, casts a warm, golden light over the landscape, as if trying to hold on to the last remnants of warmth before the cold winter sets in. In the midst of this autumnal scene stands a quaint restaurant, nestled in the picturesque town of Hout Bay, South Africa, Enter Casanova and Charles.)

Charles: One can now sense winter is around the corner; look at how many trees have now stripped of their leaves, stand bare and vulnerable against the wind, while the roses and grass, once vibrant and colourful, have now withered and turned brown.

Casanova: Yea, I can feel how the air is filled with the distinct scent of decaying leaves, reminding us that the season of growth and abundance has passed. We are half way to finishing harvesting.

(As we look out towards the ocean, we see the powerful Atlantic current, churning and frothing as it crashes against the shoreline. Seagulls soar high above the waves, calling out to each other as if in a frenzy of excitement as it crashes against the shoreline. Seagulls soar high above the waves, calling out to each other as if in a frenzy of excitement.)

Casanova: It's a bit cold and gloomy today; thank goodness for the warm glow of the restaurant's lights, which welcomes us in, and invites us to take refuge from the wind and drizzle.

(Inside, the smell of freshly cooked seafood and warm bread fills the air, while the sound of clinking glasses and laughter creates a cosy ambiance; despite the dreary weather outside, inside the restaurant, we

find comfort in the company of loved ones and the delicious food that warms our bellies.)

Charles: I just adore the sounds of the waves crashing on the rocky shore. Look at the couples around, they are just relaxing and enjoying their love in deciduous autumn, knowing it's a public holiday tomorrow.

Casanova: Tomorrow is Freedom Day?

Charles: Yes, it's the 27th April, 16 years since we had our first democratic elections. Just look how filled with love these people are, if only we all had such.

Casanova: Isn't your love with Cynthia glittering? *(Sipping some champagne.)*

Charles: We are slowly getting back on track, after all that saga. We have fixed things. But you...

Casanova: I can't believe you are still on that.

Charles: I can't believe you cheated on Precious, man. You know that she's a sister to Cynthia.

Casanova: Look, I know I messed up, but I didn't think it would be that big of a deal, and it's not like I'm the only guy who's ever cheated on a girl.

Charles: *(disgusted.)* That's not the point, Casanova. You can't just go around playing with girls' feelings like that. You need to start taking relationships seriously.

Casanova: *(defensive.)* Hey, I know I've been a player in the past. But you can't judge me for that. I don't need you telling me how to live my life. And speaking of people meddling in other people's business, your boy Bachelor needs to learn to keep his mouth shut.

Charles: *(confused.)* What are you talking about?

Casanova: (angry.) He went and blabbed about my business to everyone. How am I supposed to trust anyone now?

Charles: *(Sighs.)* Bachelor was just looking out for Cynthia's sister. He didn't want Precious to get hurt. Maybe if you weren't such a player, you wouldn't have to worry about people talking behind your back.

Casanova: Bachelor had scores to settle, he couldn't take it that I beat him for a date with Precious. He could have just come and talked to me about it. And speaking of secrets, I heard a little something about your family too.

Charles: What are you talking about?

Casanova: Your dad. I saw him the other day, when I was having lunch with Precious. He was with some other woman, not your mom. That woman is none other than Marry his colleague.

Charles: *(shocked, stopping eating.):* What? That's impossible. My parents have been married for over thirty years.

Casanova: Hey, don't shoot the messenger. I'm just telling you what I saw.

Charles: (angry.) How could you even think about bringing my family into this? That's a low blow, Casanova.

Casanova: (apologetic.) Look, I didn't mean to hurt you like that. I just got carried away. I'm sorry. I had taken you out just to have a gentleman's talk with you, not this.

Charles: (calming down.) It's fine. I just... I can't believe this is happening. My dad is cheating on my mom? It's like my whole world has been turned upside down.

Casanova: *(sympathetic.)* I know how you feel. But you have to remember, nobody's perfect. We all make mistakes. The important thing is to learn from them and try to do better next time.

Charles: *(nodding.)* Yeah, I know. I just need some time to process all of this.

Casanova: *(understanding.)* Take all the time you need. And hey, if you ever want to talk about it, I'm here for you.

Charles: I can't believe I would have been on the same page with you in the past, let alone in such incidents.

Casanova: Well, I am not that much of a dragon as you have been told I am or have known.

Exeunt

7.3.13 Scene Thirteen

(It is a gloomy autumn evening in Fish Hoek, a small coastal town with hexagon-shaped streets. Max and Leah had arranged to meet at a local coffee shop, which is nestled in a quiet corner of the town. As they made their way towards the coffee shop, they could feel the chill in the air, and hear the sound of crashing waves in the distance. Max is dressed in a thick and jeans, trying to keep warm in a chilly weather. Leah is wearing a warm, long coat, paired with a scarf and boots, as she walks alongside Max.)

Max: *(feeling his heart skip a beat.)* I am so thrilled to meet up with you, Leah. (They enter a coffee shop.)

Leah: *(Lost in thought.)* Yea... I am too. *(They sit down at a table near the window.).*

Leah: *(Thinking.)* I wish this night would end because my mind isn't here.

Max: Leah , you seem to be seemed lost in thought; and I can sense you are not pleased.

Leah: Ah?

Max: You seem a little distant.

Leah: Yeah, I'm just thinking about things. I can't stop thinking about Valentine."

Max: I know it's hard, but you need to try to move on from him." You can't keep holding onto something that's not going to happen.

Leah: I know, Max. But I can't help the way I feel. I love him so much.

Max: *(Max felt a pang of sadness in his heart as he heard Leah's words. He wished that he could tell her how he felt about her, but he didn't want to complicate things.)*

Max: Leah, I understand that you love him. But sometimes, we need to let go of things that aren't good for us. You deserve to be happy, and you won't find that by holding onto something that's not meant to be.

(Leah looked up at Max, and he could see the sadness in her eyes. He felt a sudden urge to comfort her, to hold her in his arms and tell her everything would be okay.)

Leah: I know, but I just can't let go. I love him so much, and I know he still has feelings for me too.

Max: Leah, you can't just assume that. Valentine is committed to Sharon now, and you need to respect that. You can't just try to come between them.

Leah: But Max, I know Valentine better than anyone else. I know he still loves me deep down.

Max: Even if that's true, it doesn't change the fact that he's engaged to Sharon. You can't just disregard their relationship and try to win him back.

Leah: I just don't know what to do. I can't imagine my life without him.

Max: Leah, you need to start thinking about your own well-being. You can't keep holding onto something that isn't going to happen. You need to focus on yourself and your own happiness.

Leah: I understand what you're saying, Max, but I just can't help the way I feel.

Max: I know it's hard, Leah. But you have to try to move on. It's not fair to you or anyone else involved to hold onto something that's not going to happen.

Leah: I know you're right, Max. It's just hard to let go of something I care so deeply about.

Max: I understand, Leah. But you have to start somewhere. Focus on yourself and your own happiness. And who knows, maybe someday you'll find someone who's even better for you than Valentine.

Leah: Like who?

Max: (*mumbles.*) A right person shall come for you, don't do anything stupid.

Leah: Stupid? Are you saying I am stupid?

Max: No, not at all. I am saying don't do think which shall make him despise you more. You cannot hold on to what happened some three years ago.

Leah: I don't know Max I don't know. Just do not tell Sharon about this, or anyone for that matter.

Max: Don't worry, I shall not.

Leah: Thanks. You are such a lovely man; you truly deserve a woman with integrity and honour. You always have my back.

Max: It's because I love you.

Leah: Wow, that is so sweet. You are a friend indeed, and I love you too friend.

Max :(*in thought.*) Can't she see how I really feel about her?

Leah: What? (*Smiling, puzzled.*)

Max: Nothing, I am just thinking.

Leah: Thinking about what.

Max: What you are telling me. I hope for a happy ending for all of us.

Leah: There will be. Trust me. (*Checking time*). Let me go now, I have a pile of work to do, even though it's holiday tomorrow.

Max: Cool. Let's call it a night. (*As they finished their coffee, they stand up; walk out of the coffee shop, into the cool autumn air. They said their goodbyes, with a newfound understanding between them. Max felt a glimmer of hope in his heart, as he walked away from Leah, hoping that someday, she would feel the same way about him as he did about her.*)

Exeunt

7.3.14 Scene Fourteen

(The room is dimly lit, with only a small lamp casting a soft glow on the couch where Andrews lay sound asleep. The cool autumn breeze drifted in through an open window, causing Andrews to stir in his sleep; wrapped in a warm blanket when suddenly the sound of the door opening jolted him awake. Charles walks in, staggering and clearly very drunk, with Casanova following closely behind. Suddenly, the peace was shattered by the sound of the door slamming open. Charles stumbled in, his words slurring as he tried to steady himself. Andrews sat up, rubbing his eyes in confusion.)

Andrews: *(groggily.)* Charles, what on earth are you doing here at this hour? And what has happened to you?

Charles: *(slurring.)* Dad, you won't believe it! Casanova here dropped me off, and I've had the craziest night ever.

Casanova: *(chuckles.)* Sorry about dropping him off so late, Mr. Andrews. I'll be on my way now.

Andrews: (sighs.) Where are you coming from?

Casanova: From Hout Bay, sir.

Andrews: You drove all the way from Hout Bay to Fish Hoek?

Casanova: Yes, sir. I am sorry for any inconvenience. *(Charles falls on the floor, they pick him up and put him on a couch.)*

Andrews: Alright, take care, Casanova.

(As Casanova leaves, Andrews turns back to his son, who is now looking at him with an angry expression.)

Andrews: *(concerned.)* Charles, what's wrong? You seem upset.

Charles: Don't pretend like you don't know John Andrews.

Andrews: Charles, what's going on? Are you drunk?

Charles: Dad, you wouldn't believe what just happened! Casanova dropped me off here, and I'm so drunk I can barely stand.

(*Andrews frowned, displeased with Charles' behaviour. He had never seen him drunk.*)

Andrews: Charles, this is not acceptable behaviour. You need to get your act together.

(*Charles, however, was not in the mood to listen. He had something on his mind that he needed to confront his father about.*)

Charles: Dad, why did you have an affair with Marry? Why did you cheat on Mom? (*He stands up.*)

(*Andrews was taken aback by his son's words. He had never expected to be confronted about his affair, especially not by his own son.*)

Andrews: Charles, I don't know what you're talking about. I haven't had an affair with anyone.

(*Charles, however, is not convinced. He had heard rumours about his father's affair and is determined to get to the bottom of it.*)

Charles: Don't lie to me, Dad. I know about you and Marry. Everyone at the school knows about it. You think you can make love... No, not love. Have sex in school, hang out in restaurants, and sleep in hotels with your mistress, and nobody sees you.

Andrews: Where did you get all this?

Charles: (*accusingly.*) Don't play dumb with me, dad. I heard about your little affair with Marry. How could you cheat on Mom like that?

Andrews: (*taken aback.*) What? Who told you that?

Charles: (*angrily.*) It doesn't matter who has told me! Is it true or not?

Andrews: (*defensively.*) Look, Charles, I don't know where you're getting this from, but it's not what you think. Marry and I are just friends, and there's nothing going on between us.

Charles: (*shouting.*) Don't lie to me, Dad! I've seen the way you look at her, and Mom deserves better than a cheating liar like you!

Andrews: *(upset.)* Charles, I understand that you're angry, but please don't speak to me like that. I made a mistake, and I regret it every day.

Charles: *(Upset).* Regret it every day? When are you going to tell my mother about this? Wait... I remember that day, when I came here, you and Marry seemed to have seen a ghost from the dead. She slept in my mother's bed?

Andrews: No. We have never done it here.

Charles: Just say it dad! Say where you had sex with her. And stop lying. You fucked her here.

Andrews: (Outraged.) I may have sinned, but I am still your father. You cannot speak to me like that.

Charles: *(Upset.)* When are you going to tell her?

Andrews: No, please! We can't tell her. I will lose everything.

Charles: Well, you should have thought about that before committing adultery. You even go to church, what Bible do you read? Thou shall not commit adultery Exodus 20:14; Know ye not that the unrighteous shall not inherit the kingdom of God? Be not deceived: Neither fornicators, nor idolaters, nor adulterers, nor effeminates, nor abusers of themselves with mankind, nor thieves, nor covetous, nor drunkards, nor revellers, nor extortionist, shall inherit the kingdom of God. And such were some of you: but ye are washed, but ye are sanctified, but ye are justified in the name of the Lord Jesus, and by the Spirit of our God.

(Andrews felt a pang of guilt in his heart. He had never meant to hurt his wife or his family, but his affair had spiralled out of control.)

Andrews: Charles, I made a mistake. I never meant to hurt anyone. I don't know how to explain it, but I was going through a difficult time and things just happened. I will work things out so they are the same as they were before.

(Charles gets furious. He couldn't believe that his father could be so selfish and hurtful.)

Charles: (*disbelievingly.*) Working things out? How can you work things out after what you've done? You're a hypocrite, Dad, and I can't even look at you right now.

Andrews: (*sighs.*) I know I've let you down, Charles, but please try to understand that I'm only a human, and I make mistakes just like anyone else. But I love you, and I love your mother, and I'll do whatever it takes to make things right again.

Charles: That's not good enough, Dad. You betrayed Mom's trust, and you betrayed our family. How could you do this to us?

(*Andrews felt a sense of shame wash over him as he listened to his son's words. He knew that he had made a terrible mistake, and there was no way to make things right.*)

Andrews: Charles, I'm sorry. I know that I can never undo what I've done, but I promise you that I will do everything in my power to make things right. I love your mother, and I love our family. I never meant to hurt anyone.

(*Charles shook his head, unable to forgive his father for what he had done.*)

Charles: I don't know if I can ever forgive you, Dad. You've broken our trust and our family. I need some time to think about things. (*With those words, Charles stumbled out of the room, leaving Andrews alone with his thoughts. Andrews knew that he had a long but he was determined to make things right and earn back his family's trust.*)

Exeunt

7.3.15 Scene Fifteen

(Green Point, a suburb of Cape Town located along the Atlantic Seaboard; situated near the city centre and is known for its beautiful views of the ocean and mountains.

On a brisk autumn day. The cloudy sky is filled with Stratus Clouds. The temperature is mild and cool, with a gentle breeze blowing through the air.

The trees, lining the streets, are painted in hues of golden brown, red and yellow, as the autumn leaves fall gently to the ground. The roses in the nearby gardens are still in bloom, despite the cooler weather, adding a pop of colour to the otherwise muted surroundings.

The stratus clouds slowly begin to dissipate, revealing a glimpse of blue sky. The sun breaks through the clouds, casting a warm glow over the landscape. (he trees and roses appear to come alive, basking in the sunlight, and the ocean takes on a shimmering hue.)

Casanova: You must be elated to live in such a vibrant suburb, home to the famous Green Point Stadium, which is on board to host the 2010 FIFA World Cup in the upcoming winter; popular for its vibrant nightlife, restaurants, and cafes, as well as its proximity to many popular tourist attractions such as the V&A Waterfront and the Sea Point Promenade.

Bachelor: Yes, I am highly blessed to have been born here, also owning some apartments.

Casanova: You must be making a lot of money since Green Point is such a trendy and fashionable neighbourhood, with many luxury apartments and high-end shops.

Bachelor: I agree; I have money but many other problems; additionally, you live in Hout Bay, with its majestic mountains and

194

beautiful sandy **beach.** You find an attractive harbour that has a thriving fishing community, luxurious hotels, and the World of Birds Wildlife Sanctuary and Monkey Park, which is home to thousands of birds and animals from around the world. Are you enjoying here?

Casanova: Yes, I was just driving by and passing by the trees lining the streets, which are painted in hues of golden brown, red, and yellow, as the autumn leaves fall gently to the ground. The roses in the nearby gardens are still in bloom, despite the cooler weather, adding a pop of colour to the other muted surroundings.

(*In a distance, the cold Benguela current of the Atlantic Ocean can be felt. The sea is calm, with gentle waves lapping against the shore. The water has taken on a deeper shade of blue, contrasting beautifully against the muted surroundings.*)

Bachelor: So why have you called me to meet you here in this spur? I can't even believe I am sitting here with you.

Casanova: As the idiom goes: keep your friends close but your enemies closer.

Bachelor (eating *a hake.*) I am listening.

Casanova: (*Sighs.*) I want you to tell me: What is it that you want from me?

Bachelor: I am not following.

Casanova: Why are you messing up my relationships? You keep meddling in my business.

Bachelor: What are you talking about?

Casanova: (*upset.*)Don't play dump with me, Bachelor. How could you? I can't believe you did that Bachelor! You made all of my girlfriends angry by exposing me to them.

Bachelor: You are upset with me? You are the one who has been cheating on them, you exposed yourself; they woke up and found out what kind of person you are.

Casanova: Have I exposed myself? You seem to be delighted about this?

Bachelor: It is not a matter of whether I am delighted or not; you are the one who has been cheating on all of them and playing with their emotions. You deserve to be exposed for your actions.

Casanova: What? So you deliberately sabotaged my relationships to settle your score that I beat you up on a date with Precious?

Bachelor: You are so narrow minded; I can't believe you are making this about Precious. All your girls were coming to me, frustrated and distressed about you. What was I supposed to say?

Casanova: (Confused.) Why would they come to you? Ndalo is right that you hate my guts.

Bachelor: Stop listening to that snake-that dragon, and listen to what I am telling you. I could not lie and say you are not cheating, or that they should ask you.

Casanova: That is not the point! You had no right to do that. You are always trying to bring me down and make me look bad in front of everyone.

Bachelor: As if you have not been doing that to me?

Casanova: So this is your revenge? What you did was so low.

Bachelor: No, I am trying to make you realise that what you are doing is sick, egoistical, and self-serving. You can't keep hurting people and getting away with it. You need to accept accountability and responsibility for your actions.

Casanova: You wouldn't understand. Have you ever had a girlfriend? You have always been a bachelor and a loser.

Bachelor: You can call me all sorts of names, but being a playboy, trying to be some sort of a casanova is just being self-regarding and self-absorbed.

Casanova: It's easy for you to say. You act like you have never made any mistakes.

Bachelor: I have never claimed to be perfect, but at least I am not a player like you who uses girls for your own pleasure, you need to look at yourself in the mirror and see whom to blame, you can't blame others for your actions.

Casanova: You don't understand. I can't help it if I am so charming and all the girls fall for me.

Bachelor: That is not an excuse Casanova. Look at me, I am tall in stature just as you are, 180 centimetres tall; I have got blue eyes and brown hair, with a masculine athletic body just as you, high cheek bones, and a high pitched voice. I don't do what you are doing, I have been told I am hot, but I don't play with people's emotions using my exquisiteness.

Casanova: It's because you can't express yourself and are an introvert, I am even bewildered by how explosive you are right now. What has changed?

Bachelor: I guess people change, when they encounter people like you. Your enchantment isn't an excuse to play with people's hearts. You need to learn to be faithful and treat people with respect. There is a good soul in you, but you need to grow up and face your actions.

Casanova: I do not need your lecture, and holier than thou, I know what I am doing. Perhaps it is who I am; I cannot change.

Bachelor: That is rubbish. Look at the mess you have created with these girls, using them for your own sexual gratification without caring about their emotions.

Casanova: I am a man.

Bachelor: (*inflamed.*) A man? What kind of a man are you? A man is not heartless; a man is not self-ingrained, and a man does not use women for his own pleasure then discard them. A man has logic and lives an upright lifestyle with integrity and honour. What you are saying is sexist and patriarchal.

Casanova: (*Sighs.*) I guess you are right there, but please; stop meddling in my affairs. I am still growing, have not yet explored life; have recently come out of high school, I have not yet matured, and my sexual urges are still high; with peer pressure adding on top of that. To accuse me of sexism and patriarchy is implausible and far from being analogical.

Bachelor: Actually, it is commensurable; if you cannot see that, I do not know what more to say to you. Sexism comes in all sorts of forms; beliefs, upbringing, laws, traditions, and socialisation through a variety of sociocultural institutions like the media, courts, family, education, health, religion, the economic sphere, and so forth.

Casanova: I get all that, what it is has to do with me and you sabotaging my love life.

Bachelor: *(perplexed.)* Love? I can't believe you said that; what you are doing isn't love but lust perpetuated by your own desires. As I said, you need to do a thorough self-introspection; you shall see what I am telling you. What would it take for you to change? Is it worth it and truly satisfactory to go from town to town with this woman and that woman? You know, the eye is not satisfied with seeing, and the ear is not satisfied with hearing; is it worth it to see and hear all things?

Casanova: No it is not, and derailing.

Bachelor: Well then that's it. *(there is silence, they take some glass of granadilla juice, then Sharon enters.)*

Sharon: Hi.

Both: Hi.

Sharon: Bachelor, I have been trying to reach your brother, and is not home, where is he?

Bachelor: I don't know, he mentioned something about going to Simon's Town.

Sharon: To do what?

Bachelor: I am not sure; I am not sure.

Sharon: *(looking at Casanova.)* Hi, are you one of his cousin?

Casanova:(bewildered.) Who?

Sharon: Bachelor

Casanova: No, not even close, I am Casanova Smith from Hout Bay; I attended high school with him.

Sharon: (*Her heart pounds harder.*) Oh. I must have mistaken because of the resemblance.

Casanova: You are not the first one.

Bachelor: This is Sharon, my brother's fiancée; they just got engaged last month.

Casanova: Congratulations.

Sharon: (*Curious.*) Can I sit?

Both: Sure, you can.

(*She sits*)

Exeunt

7.3.16 Scene Sixteen

(Simon's Town, a home to Naval Base Simon's Town[1], the South African Navy[2]'s largest base, is located on the shores of False Bay[3], on the eastern side of the Cape Peninsula[4].
The land rises steeply from near the water's edge, with the town is boxed in along the shoreline by the heights above. The small harbour is protected from swells by a breakwater[5]s built with thousands of huge blocks of sandstone quarried out of the face of the mountain above. The Simon's Town railway station[6] is the terminus of the Southern Line[7], it runs south of the central business district of Cape Town, then along the steep eastern shore of False Bay. In a family home, on a partially cloudy day, Delilah walks in, sitting in the lounge.)

Delilah: If this plan works, my daughter will marry Valentine, and I will make sure she marries in the community of property so that she can own all things owned by him, including shares and those luxurious properties of the Green Family. All that wealth was supposed to be mine if Bridget had not taken Richard from me. With that, I could invest and attain a lot in Simon's Town free port

1. https://en.wikipedia.org/wiki/Naval_Base_Simon%27s_Town

2. https://en.wikipedia.org/wiki/South_African_Navy

3. https://en.wikipedia.org/wiki/False_Bay

4. https://en.wikipedia.org/wiki/Cape_Peninsula

5. https://en.wikipedia.org/wiki/Breakwater_(structure)

6. https://en.wikipedia.org/wiki/Simon%27s_Town_railway_station

7. https://en.wikipedia.org/wiki/Southern_Line_(Cape_Town)

and reap immensely from the special economic zone[8] for better trade[9] and commerce[10] deals.

(Inflicted.) I am so sorry, Richard; I did not mean for any of this to happen. It was that woman who was supposed to be the target, not you.

(Cries.) And now I have to live with this guilt for the rest of my life. I hope you find a way to forgive me for ending your life like that. Those fools ruined everything and did the opposite of what I told them to do, but then, crying over spilt milk will not help.

(Sighs.) What is done is done, there is no turning back. I just hope now that the cards play right. (A doorbell rings.) I wonder who that is. I am not expecting anyone; Leah did not say she was coming. Let me go check. (She goes, then Valentine is at the door; she is shocked and confused.) Hi.

Valentine: Hello. May I come in?

Delilah: Who are you?

Valentine: Hallo, ma'am. I am Green. Valentine Green, from Green Point.

Delilah: Oh, I see. Are you the son of Richard?

Valentine: Yes, I am.

Delilah: (Thrilled.) Come in, come in!"

Valentine: Thanks.

(He comes in.)

Delilah: You may sit. Can I get you anything to drink?

Valentine: (sitting.)"No, thank you.

Delilah: How is everything?

Valentine: Everything is fine, it's going well.

Delilah: (nervous.) What brings you here?

---

8. https://en.wikipedia.org/wiki/Special_economic_zone

9. https://en.wikipedia.org/wiki/Trade

10. https://en.wikipedia.org/wiki/Commerce

Valentine: I want your assistance, please. I have been thinking about my long-lost brother.

Delilah: *(feeling guilty.)* You had a brother?

Valentine: Yes, I had two, actually. They were twins, but the other one got lost.

Delilah: *(Heart beating intensely.)* So how may I help you?

Valentine: If you can, please tell me of any child or children adopted in 1993 at the orphanage centre you worked at.

Delilah: *(shivering.)* I am sorry, I can't. There was plenty going on at that time. It was an intense and violent time in our country. There were plenty of orphans at that time. I don't even know where they could be now.

Valentine: Please just try to remember, somewhere around winter. I was speaking with my uncle, and he said you worked in some orphanage at the time Helen Smith happened to adopt a child.

Delilah: *(shuttering and shivering.)* But what does that have to do with your brother's lost twin?

Valentine: What I mean is, I have heard how some guy named Casanova resembles him, and you would think they are cousins or brethren.

Delilah: This is so invasive—so you have been digging up information about me?

Valentine: No, not at all. I just need to find him. You know, when I was at Helen's Hotel, I bumped into some guy, tall in stature, who was arguing with some girls; he looked like my younger brother, and it happened so fast, I couldn't look at him thoroughly or speak to him.

Delilah: Maybe you are just frustrated and thinking a lot about him. What confuses me is why you would think Helen has your adopted brother, and how do I get involved in this?

Valentine: For you to give me the name of the orphanage centre and date of the adoption of Helen's son.

Delilah: *(fearing.)* I am sorry I can't help you; firstly, it is unethical; secondly, that orphanage facility is non-existent now; it's been over 17 years since. I am also not certain if Helen adopted his child from where I worked. *(She stands up.)* I think I have given you all the information that I know; would you please excuse me?

Valentine: *(standing up):* Please, ma'am, if you can recall anything.

Delilah: I have told you what I know. Your brother could even be in the Eastern Cape, Limpopo, or anywhere across the country or even outside the country. You can never be certain who he is or where he is. I have somewhere to go. Please excuse me.

Valentine: *(senses something is wrong.)* I am sorry for bothering you. But if you have any information, please contact me here. (Giving her a business card.)

Delilah: Okay, I will. (She takes the card, then she walks him out to the gate.) Goodbye.

Valentine: Stay well. *(Delilah closes the gates and locks them; Valentine gets inside a car and drives away.)*

Delilah: *(frustrated and shivering.)* My goodness, what am I going to do? What are we going to do? This is going to end badly. Let me touch Helen.

Exit

7.3.17 Scene Seventeen

(Fish Hoek, False Bay College, in the afternoon, a parking area; enter Paul and Rose.)

Paul: What you have done is unacceptable, we let you out of the house to study, not to gallivant around the entire city of Cape Town. For that, you even slept at Bachelor' home, without Valentine knowing.

Rose: "I am sorry, dad." But please believe me when I say that nothing happened between me and Bachelor.

Paul: I am just wondering, if you don't even have any friends. What were you even doing in Hout Bay? To see a boy? That was so low, my child; you degraded yourself.

Rose: That is so harsh. I am sorry; it shall not happen again.

Paul: "You have truly disappointed me." I am highly dissatisfied and disappointed in you. You are doing your own nonsense, Max is doing his crap partying and hardly gets home, I don't even know where he lives in this Fish Hoek. You and your brother should put yourselves together.

Rose: "I am so sorry, dad." But you and mother aren't there, the house is cold. I don't even know what she's doing in the CBD.

Paul: *(Afflicted.)* All shall be well my child. (***Embracing her.***) Let me go for now, to calm down. I'll see you. *(He goes.)*

Rose: *(Afflicted.)*My goodness! I am not just worried about how this has been exposed, but if Casanova will come to his senses and see how much I love him. I feel such intense emotional trauma, my heart feels like it's being stamped by a hippopotamus; I can't breath properly.

(Amanda enters.)

Amanda: (*inflamed.*) I finally got you.

Rose: What is it, Amanda?

Amanda: What are you doing with my boyfriend?

Rose: What boyfriend?

Amanda: Don't play dump with me, girl; you know exactly whom I am talking about.

Rose: "I don't know what you're talking about."

Amanda: (Angry.) You think I don't know you have been seeing Casanova behind my back?

Rose: Oh, him? Yes, I knew, so what? It's not like you are the only girl he has hooked up with.

Amanda: What? He promised me that it would never happen again.

Rose: I guess you've been duped, just like the rest of us, unless you're like me and got into a relationship knowing exactly what kind of person he is.

Amanda: (*slaps her.*) You bloody snake. I thought you were my friend.

(*Other students nearby notice the conflict.*)

1ˢᵗ **Student**: What the hell are they fighting about?

2ⁿᵈ **Student:** You mean you do not know?

1ˢᵗ **Student:** Know what?

3ʳᵈ **Student:** They have been played by Casanova, I am sure you remember him from Fish Hoek High School.

1ˢᵗ **Student:** What is it with you girls fighting over a guy? I am certain that Casanova doesn't love any of these. (*Rose laps back, they get into a fight.*)

Rose: You are such a whore. (They strangle one another; the First Student comes in and resolves the fight.)

1ˢᵗ Student: What is it with you? Fighting over a guy, a moron who does not love any of you,

(Aside)

Second Student: It is even worse, this Casanova has been dating Precious, a pupil at Fish Hoek High School, currently in grade 12.

1st Student: You mean Precious, who is Cynthia's sister?

2nd Student: The one and only. *(In an instance, Casanova arrives.)* Look, speak of the devil. Here he comes.

Casanova: Guys, what are you doing? This is so hooligan and not ladylike.

Amanda and Rose: *(slapping him.)* How dare you!

Amanda: We are in this mess because of you!

Casanova: Even you, Rose?" We are through!

Rose: *(Shocked.)* What?

Casanova: You too, Amanda.

Amanda: But, babe. *(Disappointed.)*

Rose: How can you do this to me? (Many students gather.)

Casanova: We are done!

Rose: What have I done wrong?

Casanova: In as much as I am at fault here, the behaviour from both of you is highly displeasing, this is devaluing yourselves. (Some students are *laughing, some are cheering, and some are shocked.)* I am sorry, guys, that it has to end like this.

Rose: (disheartened.) After all that we have been through, you spit me out like a sucked and chewed mango in autumn.

Amanda: You are so cruel. You even do this here? You are such a self-ingrained despicable person.

Casanova: Yes, I take all those words, and I've realised I need to do some introspection and do things differently with girls. I am again sorry guys, but we are done.

Exeunt

7.3.18 Scene Eighteen

(The air is cool and crisp, and with the sky scattered with stratocumulus clouds and the sun beginning to dip below the horizon, the stadium lights flickered to life, illuminating the field and casting a warm glow over the Green Point Stadium in Cape Town, South Africa. It is on Freedom Day, the 27th of April 2010, and thousands of people have gathered to watch the soccer match between Ghana and South Africa.

As the stadium filled up, the excited chatter of fans echoed through the air, punctuated by the occasional roar of a vuvuzela. The green of the field contrasted sharply with the blue and white stripes of the South African flag that flutters in the breeze from the Atlantic Ocean.

The sky is a canvas of grey and white, with Stratocumulus clouds slowly moving overhead, casting shadows over the stadium. The smell of freshly cut grass mixed with the aroma of various foods being sold by vendors, creating a unique sensory experience.

As the players warmed up on the field, the crowd erupted into cheers, each side vying for their team to come out on top. The energy is palpable, and the anticipation of the match builds with each passing moment.

Bachelor, attending the match for the first time, had recently struck up a conversation with two new friends, Matthew and Sithabile. They are standing together, wearing matching South African sports jerseys, and chatting animatedly about the game.)

Bachelor: So, what do you guys think? Is South Africa going to take it? *(His eyes glued to the field.)*

Sithabile: (shrugging.) It's hard to say. Ghana is a tough team. But I think we have a good shot.

Matthew: (nodded in agreement.) Yeah, I'm feeling pretty optimistic. The boys have been training hard. I believe both Ghana and South Africa will do greatly in the upcoming FIFA World Cup in June.

(As they speak, the stadium is filling up with fans, their colourful flags and banners waving in the breeze, with the sound of vuvuzelas filling the air, adding to the already buzzing energy of the crowd.)

Bachelor: (astounded) I can't stop myself from being thrilled and elated; you're such good company.(*excited as he gazes around at the sea of people.*) I have not felt such camaraderie and excitement in a long time.

(As the sun continued its slow descent, casting an orange glow over the stadium, the three friends settled in for what promised to be an unforgettable match.)

Sithabile: You are so funny, and warmly welcoming too; I couldn't be anywhere else than here.

Bachelor: Hey guys, have you seen that girl over there? The one with the curly hair and the yellow shirt? I think she's really cute. (*Drinking beer.*)

Sithabile: Yeah, I see her. You should go talk to her.

Matthew: Definitely, man. Don't be shy. You never know what could happen.

Bachelor: I don't know, guys. I'm not good at approaching girls. What if she rejects me?

Sithabile: What if she doesn't? You'll never know if you don't try.

Matthew: "Yeah, and we'll be here to support you." Just go for it.

Bachelor: (nervously.) I don't know—what if she's not interested? What if I embarrass myself?

Sithabile: Just be yourself, man. You're a cool guy, and I'm sure she'll see that. Plus, you'll never know unless you try.

Matthew: And hey, if it doesn't work out, we're still here to hang out with you. No pressure.

Bachelor: *(taking a deep breath.)* Okay, you're right. I'm going to go for it. You guys convinced me. Wish me luck.

(As Bachelor makes his way towards the girl, another young woman approaches the group.)

Candies: Hey guys, what's up? My name is Candies. I'm from Cape Flats.

Sithabile: Hey, nice to meet you. I'm Sithabile, and these are my friends Bachelor and Matthew.

Candies: Cool, so you guys are here for the match too? It's been intense so far, right?

Matthew: Yeah, definitely. It's been a nail-biter. Right now, it's tied at 2-2.

Candies: Wow, that's crazy. You know, my friend Grace is really into soccer. She's been talking about this match for weeks.

Bachelor: *(perking up.)* Grace? Is she the one over there? (*He points to the girl* he *has been eyeing.)*

Candies: Oh, yeah, that's her. Do you want me to introduce you?

Bachelor: (smiling.) Yeah, that would be great. Thanks, Candies.

(As Candies leads the group over to Grace, they all grab some beers and sit down at one of the luxurious tables and chairs nearby. The camaraderie between the group is palpable, with everyone chatting and laughing as they watch the match together.)

Grace: So, are you guys enjoying the soccer match?

Sithabile: Yeah, it's been great so far. South Africa is doing pretty well.

Matthew: Yeah, but Ghana is putting up a good fight.

Candies: It's a good thing we're all here celebrating Freedom Day together. It's important to remember our history and how far we've come.

(As the sun begins to dip below the horizon, the stadium lights flickered to life, illuminating the field and casting a warm glow over the

fans. It is a moment of unity and celebration, as people from all walks of life came together to enjoy the sport and commemorate the hard-won freedoms of their country.)

Bachelor: Definitely. Apartheid was the most atrocious, fragmented, and worst policy ever in our country. I'm actually really glad I met you guys. You all seem really cool.

Grace: "Aw, thanks." You seem pretty cool too.

Sithabile: Hey, do you guys want to go grab a drink or something after the game?

Matthew: Yeah, that sounds like a great idea.

Candies: I'm down for that. What do you two think, Grace and Bachelor?

Bachelor: Sounds good to me.

Grace: I'm in.

(The group gets up from their seats and heads towards the exit, chatting and laughing together.)

Exeunt

7.3.19 Scene Nineteen

(Green Point, a family home; enter Valentine and Sharon)

Valentine: I went to Simon's Town today to see that woman.

 Sharon: And?

Valentine: (Worried.) I couldn't find any information. I could see that she did not want to help. I feel so defeated; I do not know what to do.

Sharon: I am so sorry; it must be hard; You had taken a long time to grieve for your own parents, and now this comes; it must be inflicting indeed.

Valentine: It is, very much. I had hopes, I would find Matthew. Maybe I should speak to her daughter. (Recalling.) You know, when I was there at Helen's Hotel, I bumped into this guy; he truly resembled Bachelor. I couldn't speak to him, nor gaze at him thoroughly as he was being kicked outside with some girls. Could it be him?

Sharon: You know, today; I was in town, in this restaurant. I happened to bump into Bachelor in deep conversation with some guy, I went and sat with them. He said he was Casanova. I can now attest that he truly resembles both of you.

Valentine: Then let's find him. He could be Helen's adopted son, and I suspect he might be the lost twin.

Sharon: And say what? Let's not do something that will scare him away, and if it is true that Helen and this Delilah woman are hiding something; they will ensure you do not get him, maybe even take him away from Cape Town even. We've come up with a bigger plan.

Valentine: (frustrated.) Like what? Do you have any ideas?

Sharon: Look, when I was there, I stole the glass and fork Casanova was drinking and eating with.

Valentine: (Confused.) How will that help?

Sharon: DNA test. " We need to be certain that he is truly Bachelor's twin. Here they are. (*She opens her bag and takes them out.*)

Valentine: (Excited.) Thank you, love; this is why I love you so much. (Kisses her.) How are we going to do it? Should we tell Bachelor?

Sharon: Not now; let's be 100% sure that he is before you even tell him he has a twin. Also, Casanova, had something itching him on his head, I happened to scratch him, and his hair fell out accidentally. I have it.

Valentine: That's brilliant love; I am sure it is from God.

Sharon: I know it's a lot to keep from the Bachelor, but you don't want to burden him with the fact that he lost a twin, who might be alive or dead somewhere out there, but you're just suspicious this guy might be him.

Valentine: I guess you are right. It's too heavy for him to take, he does not even have a picture of what our parents looked like except in photos. Now this would cripple his heart. Let's first find out if they are indeed twins.

Sharon: True indeed. Let's get anything of Bachelor we can use.

Valentine: His tooth brush. Go get in his bathroom before he comes back. I am sure you can find his hair there as well. I will call my friend, who is a doctor, and see if he can help.

Sharon: Let me go get them." (*She goes upstairs*).

Valentine: (*Valentine paced nervously around the sitting room, the lounge, and the kitchen, then back and forth. He gazes out the window at the dark and cloudy sky, the Altostratus clouds obscuring the moon and casting an eerie glow over the city below. He clutched his Apple iPad tightly in his hand, taking a deep breath before dialling his friend's number).* I need to get to the bottom of this. Hey Luke, it's me. *(Call being picked up.)* I need your help.

Luke: Valentine? Hallo, what's going on? You do not sound so well.

Valentine*: (Frustration lacing his voice.)* It's my brother, Bachelor, there are rumours of him resembling some guy, and whom we suspect might be his lost twin.

Luke: *(Shocked.)* Why didn't you tell me this before? Bachelor had a twin?

Valentine: Yes. It's a long story, which I will tell you another day, but help me with it, please.

Luke: Okay, I am listening.

Valentine: My fiancé met them both earlier today, and she thinks they look alike. She even managed to grab some hair from Casanova's head and a fork and glass he used. I need to get them tested for DNA.

Luke: (Sighs on the other end of the line.) Valentine, you know I can't just get you a DNA test like that. There are protocols we have to follow.

Valentine: I know, I know, *(running a hand through his hair.)* But I need to know the truth. I need to know if Bachelor's twin might still be alive, we lost it in such a horrendous way, when it was kidnapped the day our parents were murdered

Luke: (Tone softens.) Okay, okay, let me see what I can do. Bring me the samples tomorrow, and I'll see if I can get them tested.

Valentine: *(letting out a relieved breath.)* Thank you. Thank you so much. I just need to know the truth; you know? I need to know if he might the one.

Luke: I understand, but try not to get your hopes up too much. It might not be what you're expecting.

Valentine: (*Voice intense.*) I know, but I have to try. I owe it to Bachelor and our parents to find out the truth. I can't just sit here and wonder. I have to know for sure.

Luke: Okay, cool. Bring them tomorrow.

Valentine: Thank you, Luke, you are a friend indeed. (*Sharon, comes back*). I will keep in touch. (*The call ends, and Valentine sank down onto his couch, feeling a mix of frustration and hope swirling inside him. He couldn't wait for tomorrow to come.*)

Sharon: What did he say?

Valentine: He said he was going to do it.

Sharon: That's great. Finally, we will know the truth, if turns out he not, then at least you tried.

Valentine: (*eyes filled with.*) Yes, for sure. (*Sharon comes and embraces him.*)

Sharon: All is going to be alright.

Valentine: Thank you. Did you manage to get them?

Sharon: Yes. Here they are. I will put them in separate plastic bags.

Valentine: Go to the drawer there; I have some there. (*She goes and takes the plastic outs, puts Casanova's hair, glass, and fork on their own, and Bachelor's tooth brush and hair on their own.*)

Sharon: "Yeah, it's done. (Giving them to Valentine.)

Valentine: Thank you so much. I have been thinking.

Sharon: what?

Valentine: To go to jail. to see my parents' murderers.

Sharon: Why?

Valentine: Before you came up with this idea, I wanted to go see them, tell me the truth about why they murdered my father and my mother, and where exactly they dropped my brother Matthew-Bachelor's twin.

Sharon: Well, you have my full support. As the doctor said, the result might not be what you had in mind. It's better to also find other ways of getting the truth. So while you send these samples to get tested and wait for the result, go there.

Exeunt

7.3.20 Scene Twenty

(The night sky is filled with towering cumulus clouds, casting intermittent shadows on the brightly lit hotel office. Helen sat behind her desk, sorting through some paperwork, while Delilah stood in front of her, looking rather anxious.)

Delilah: Helen, I need your help with something. In fact, the time has come for the plot.

Helen: Sure, what is it?

Delilah: As I said, I want to create a situation that will make it look like Valentine slept with Leah in your hotel. This would cause tension with Sharon, to whom he is engaged.

Helen: What?! Delilah, that's outrageous! Why would you want to do that? We have spoken about this.

Delilah: I have my reasons. You see, I want my daughter Leah to marry Valentine in a community of property so that she can attain wealth and money, not just for herself but for me as well.

Helen: That's not a good enough reason to ruin someone's reputation and cause heartache for Sharon.

Delilah: But Helen, think about it. Valentine is a wealthy man, and if he marries my daughter, she will be set for life. And besides, Sharon will eventually find out that he's not faithful to her, so it's better to do it now before they get married. I told you they were once involved, some three years ago or so.

Helen: I'm sorry, Delilah, but I cannot help you with this. It's wrong, and I won't be a part of it.

Delilah: Oh, I see. Well, I guess I'll just have to find another way to make this happen.

Helen: Please, Delilah. Don't do something you'll regret.

Delilah: Oh, but I won't regret it, Helen. In fact, I have some information that might change your mind.

Helen: What information?

Delilah: Stop playing dump with me. You know, I know your little secret, Helen. We both know that your son, Casanova, is actually Valentine's brother. And not only that, but he's also the twin of Bachelor, who got lost in 1992 when Valentine's parents were murdered.

Helen: please don't do this. Blackmail is a criminal offense. For all these years, you've waiting to blackmail me?

Delilah: Just as you benefited from Richard and Bridget's murder, with all this wealth you've generated over the years,so do I want some portion of it. Now, if you don't help me with my plan, I'll be forced to reveal this information to everyone. Think about it, Helen. Do you really want this secret to be exposed? Think about it. How shall it look? Will you not be seen as the actual murderer of Richard and Bridget Green, thereafter kidnapped their son for 18 years?

(Helen sat there in shock, unable to comprehend what was happening. She couldn't believe that Delilah would stoop so low to blackmail her.)

Helen: You can't do this, Delilah. You can't force me to compromise my values.

Delilah: I'm not forcing you, Helen. I'm simply giving you a choice. Help me, or suffer the consequences.

(Helen sat there in silence, unsure of what to do. She knew Delilah could do anything to get what she wanted.)

Helen: Fine, I'll help you. But you have to promise not to tell anyone about Casanova and Bachelor.

Delilah: Of course, Helen. I always keep my promises. We shall do the deed on Friday, the 7th of May.

(Helen couldn't believe what she was doing, but she knew she had no other choice. She made a mental note to stop Delilah's plan before it was too late.)

EXUENT

7.4 Act Four
7.4.1 Scene One

(As days passed. in the morning, the last day of the second month of autumn-April, in the beautiful coastal town of Hout Bay, Cape Town, South Africa. As the sun has risen over the horizon, illuminating the sky with shades of orange and pink, it contrasts against the wispy white clouds that lazily drift across the sky. Despite the looming clouds, the temperature remains mild, providing the perfect weather for outdoor activities. The ocean's deep blue colour is mesmerizing, and it's easy to see why Hout Bay is a popular tourist destination for those seeking adventure and relaxation. Enter Charles and Casanova in an apartment, on a balcony, looking over the streets, beach, and ocean.)

Charles: It is such a beautiful day, we can feel summer has ended; the vegetation is lush and green, with trees and shrubs displaying a beautiful array of warm colours.

Casanova: Indeed. The cool breeze that sweeps across is a sign of the cold Benguela current that flows from the Atlantic Ocean, keeping the weather mild and refreshing.

(*As the morning progresses, the clouds gather, forming large clusters that cast shadows over the town. The air is filled with the sound of birds chirping and leaves rustling in the wind, creating a serene and peaceful atmosphere.*)

Casanova: (*pauses for a moment.*) Speaking of refreshing, it makes me think about a lot of things.

Charles: Speaking of things, what you did was uncalled for. How can you ditch those ladies like that?

Casanova: It wasn't my intention; it just happened. I can't believe they fought over me like that in front of everyone, worst of all college students. They acted like primary school girls. They were fighting over me, and I couldn't handle it anymore. I had to end it.

Charles: But you played them. Dumping them in public like that at False Bay College was cold bro...

Casanova: Absolutely, I now acknowledge the pain I have caused, but then they were fighting over me, and I couldn't handle it anymore. I had to end it.

Charles: That's not a good enough excuse. You could have handled it differently. You humiliated them in front of everyone.

Casanova: I know, I messed up. But things have changed for me, man. Bachelor has brought some sense to me. I want to stop being a player and settle down.

Charles: *(Surprised.)* What? I can't believe it. I mean, you've been a player for as long as I've known you.

Casanova: I know, man. But Bachelor made me realize that there's more to life than just women. And I can't keep listening to Ndalo, he's the one fuelling the conflict between me and Bachelor. Sylvia has been right, you've all been rights.

Charles: That's good to hear, Casanova. I hope you stick to your word and stop breaking women's hearts. Have you heard of heartbreak syndrome, where your heart strings tear and lose form?

Casanova: I will, man. And speaking of hearts, how are you holding up after your father's affair?

(As the day continues, the clouds grow thicker and the wind begins to pick up, signalling the possibility of rain later in the day. But for now, the town is alive with activity, with people going about their daily routines and enjoying the beautiful scenery and mild weather that make Hout Bay such a charming and alluring place to be.)

Charles: I'm not doing too well, to be honest. I'm highly displeased with my father right now. I'll only forgive him if he confesses to my mother. I still can't even swallow that he cheated on my mother with Ndalo's mother. Your friend!

Casanova: That's tough, man. I hope your father comes clean soon.

Charles: Yeah, me too. Thanks for asking, Casanova. Thank you for allowing me to stay in your apartment for a few days. I just couldn't stand looking at my father.

Casanova: Cool, it's a pleasure.

Exeunt

7.4.2 Scene Two

(The camera pans over the bustling scene outside the modern building in Green Point, Cape Town, South Africa. The sky above is filled with stratus clouds, a sign of the autumn season. The camera then turns towards the building, and we see a sign above the entrance that reads "Green Point Broadcasting".

As we move inside, we see a flurry of activity. The room is filled with the latest, high-tech broadcasting equipment. Cameras, microphones, and computer screens are scattered throughout the room. In one corner, there is a soundproof booth where a technician is testing a microphone. In another corner, there is a group of camera operators discussing the best angle for a shot.

The crew is made up of professionals who are experts in their fields. There are directors, producers, camera operators, sound engineers, and makeup artists, all working together to create the perfect broadcast. The atmosphere is one of excitement and anticipation as everyone prepares for the start of the live broadcast.)

Bachelor: Hey Sithabile, great to see you here! I'm a bit nervous about this TV show I'm going to be broadcasting. (*As the camera moves through the room, we see everyone dressed in professional attire, with some crew members wearing headsets so they can communicate with each other during the broadcast. The air is filled with the sound of people talking and the hum of electronic equipment.*)

Sithabile: Hey, man, don't be nervous. You'll do great. You seem to be passionate about sports and unity, and that's what this show is all about."

Bachelor: Yeah, you're right. I just hope I can articulate my thoughts clearly.

Sithabile: Of course, you can. Just be yourself and speak from your heart. You're a natural leader, and people will listen to you. I have watched your YouTube videos; they are well-articulated. (*Outside, we see the wind blowing in from the Atlantic Ocean, bringing with it a refreshing breeze. It's a beautiful day in Green Point, and the crew is excited to be broadcasting from this stunning location.*)

Bachelor: Thanks for the encouragement, Sithabile. Speaking of hearts, I've been meaning to talk to you about something. You remember Grace, right? The girl we met at Green Point Stadium during South Africa vs. Ghana soccer match?

Sithabile: Of course, I remember her. You like her, don't you?

Bachelor: Yeah, I do. But I'm not sure how to express my feelings to her. I don't want to make things awkward between us.

Sithabile: Don't be afraid, man. You're always fortifying your heart, and it's time to let go. Just be honest and speak from your heart. You never know, she might feel the same way about you. But what's stopping you from telling her how you feel?

Bachelor: What I went through with Casanova, that guy would grab every girl I was into.

Sithabile: I may not know Casanova, but the world is filled with guys like him; moreover; don't worry about him or any other guy; you can't let other people control your life. You need to be true to yourself and follow your heart. If you like Grace, tell her. You don't want to miss out on an opportunity to be with someone you care about...

Bachelor: You're right, Sithabile. Thanks for the push. I'll try to open up to her.

Sithabile: That's the spirit, Bachelor. You deserve to be happy, and I can tell Grace is a great girl. Don't let introversion hold you back. Be free, and let love lead the way.

Bachelor: That's encouraging indeed. You have opened my eyes to see things differently. Thanks, Sithabile. I appreciate your advice.

I'm going to take a chance and tell Grace how I feel, take her out on a date or to dinner.

Sithabile: That's the spirit, Bachelor. Be confident and believe in yourself. I know things will work out for you in the end.

(*The director comes towards them.*)

Director: Are you ready?

Bachelor: Absolutely. I am over the moon and acute about this.

Director: Go take a seat. He goes. *As the clock ticks closer to the start of the broadcast, the excitement in the room intensifies. Everyone is ready to show the world what they can do, and the viewers at home are in for a treat. (The countdown begins, and the camera fades to black as the music plays, signalling the start of the broadcast.)*

Exeunt

7.4.3 Scene Three

(In the afternoon, Valentine enters the prison to see the prisoner who murdered his parents, feeling a mix of emotions as he recalls the pain and loss he's experienced. (As he enters the cell, he sees the prisoner, who's been incarcerated for 18 years.)

Valentine: Good afternoon

Prisoner: Yes, good afternoon.

Valentine: Do you remember me?

Prisoner: No. Who are you?

Valentine: *(Sighs.)* I am Valentine Green.

Prisoner: I don't know you.

Valentine: I am Valentine Green. When I was fifteen years old, you and your partner came to our family home in the mid-winter of 1992 and murdered my parents. The same crime that led you here.

Prisoner: (Shuttered.) I am so sorry. It was not my intention.

Valentine: I came to speak with you about my parents' murder.

Prisoner: I have nothing to say to you.

Valentine: I understand why you wouldn't want to talk about it. But I need answers. Who orchestrated their murder?

Prisoner: I don't know.

Valentine: Come on, you must know something. They were my parents, and I need to know who did this to them. Who sent you?

Prisoner: I'm sorry, but I can't help you. I've been here for 18 years, and I've already told the authorities everything I know.

Valentine: What about my brother? You took him from us. Where did you drop him? off

Prisoner: I dropped him at the Vredehoek Orphanage Centre.

Valentine: And then what happened? Did you see anyone else with you during the murder?

Prisoner: No, it was me and my friend... but I remember someone telling me to do it. I didn't want to do it, but they threatened me. I didn't know who it was.

Valentine: Can you give me any more details?

Prisoner: I'm sorry, that's all I know. But if you're looking for answers, talk to a woman named Delilah Osmond. She worked at the orphanage centre in 1992 and may know more.

Valentine: (*shocked.*) Thank you. I'll do that. I just hope I can finally get some closure and find out who's responsible for all of this. (*As Valentine leaves the cell, he feels a mix of relief and sadness. He knows that he's one step closer to getting the answers he's been looking for, but he also knows that the road ahead will be difficult and painful. He's determined to find out the truth and bring justice to his family.*)

Exeunt

7.4.4 Scene Four

(Fish Hoek, it is twilight. The sun is setting over the horizon, leaving the sky with shades of orange and scarlet, Cumulus clouds are scattered across the sky. A family home, enter Charles and Andrews.)

Charles: I can't believe you did that, and you don't want to face the consequences of your infidelity.

Andrews: *(sighs.)* Son, I have apologised; I said I am so sorry. I was not thinking straight when I had an affair with Marry. I will forever regret that.

Charles: It is not me you have to apologise to. Apologise to your wife, my mother. We can't sweep this under the carpet.

Andrews: I know, but would this not then do more harm than good?

Charles: It does not matter. I cannot sit and let this go; I will not lie to my mother in front of her face. I would feel guilty myself. Mother is coming tonight, tell her I will tell her myself.

Andrews: I said I was sorry.

Charles: I know you are sorry, but we cannot build our family upon lies, father. The truth always comes out; just look at the way I found out. I was highly heartbroken, inflicted, shocked, and highly displeased with you.

Andrews: *(sadly.)* I know, son. I'll do anything to make things right.

Charles: *(Inflicted.)* Just do it, dad. Do it while it is still early and confess your sins.

(Cries): I do not want to lose this family. I know you and your mother have had such a disconnection for a long time, but I did not expect this.

Andrews: I am deeply sorry. I beg your pardon. My heart is filled with sorrow and infliction from the damage I have done. I almost lost my career for nonsense, just because I could not control my lustfulness. *(He embraces him.)*

Charles: This has ripped my heart out, father, and brought a wreath of despair. (Crying.)

Andrews: I can't apologise enough. Please accept my sincerest apologies. I am at fault and take full responsibility. Please forgive me.

(Mrs. Andrew enters.)

Mrs. Andrews: Good evening, boys. (Smiling, then surprised by the tense atmosphere in the room.)

Charles: Mother *(elated.)* I have missed much. (He hugs her, and she hugs him.)

Mrs Andrews: What's going on? Is everything okay? (There is silence and awkwardness.)

Exeunt

7.4.5 Scene Five

(In the evening, the sun has gone down; the sky deepens in a deep shade of navy, the lights of the CBD glitter, distorting the shining the stars across the partially cloudy starry heavens, enter Bachelor, Grace, Candie, Matthew and Sithabile, they are walking by the Cape Town commercial harbour.)

Bachelor: It was truly enthralling that day, we had such a pleasant day.

Matthew: True indeed, we truly had much fun. We should attend such merrymaking events again.

Candies: Absolutely, we can even go watch a cricket match or horse racing.

Bachelor: Horse racing. I love it very much.

Grace: Really? (*smiling, walking beside him.*) I love it too. I have always longed to go to the Durban July Festival, but have not had the time or logistics to do so.

Bachelor: I can arrange for that if time and means are on our side.

Sithabile: You two seem to get along.

Grace: Sure we are, Bachelor is fun to hang out with, and I like his calmness and enthusiasm about illuminating things.

Bachelor: (*Excited.*) Thank you, enjoy your company too. Thank goodness I went to that match and met you.

(Aside.)

Sithabile: Guys, let us hasten our feet a bit, and let these two talk. Their spirits seem to be glued to one another.

Candies: Great idea.

(*Sithabile, Matthew, and Candies walk fast, leaving Grace and Bachelor a few metres behind.*)

Bachelor: I love coming here. The view of the city is breath-taking. (*Bachelor walks with Grace, along the Cape Town Harbour. It is dark, and the city lights illuminate the Dutch and British architecture and postmodern architecture around them. The sky is clear and crystal, and the stars shine through, distorted by the overwhelming city lights, a cooling breeze blows by as the days are getting cooler.*)

Grace: Yeah, I agree. I come here often to clear my mind.

Bachelor: I didn't know you were into architecture. I've always found it fascinating.

Grace: Yeah, I love the mix of old and new buildings in this city. It's like a history lesson in architecture.

Bachelor: I couldn't agree more. Have you ever been to the National Gallery?

Grace: Yes, I have. I love exploring the different art exhibits.

Bachelor: That's amazing. I've been meaning to go but haven't found the time.

Grace: We should go together sometime.

Bachelor: That sounds like a great idea. Maybe we can explore the city some more after that.

Grace: I'd love that. There are so many hidden gems in this city that I haven't explored yet.

Bachelor: Same here. I've always wanted to try out some of the local cuisines. Have you ever had a biltong?

Grace: Of course! It's South African cuisine. Have you tried it?

Bachelor: I'm down for that. There is that one, which Xhosa people call isidudu; made of a mixture of boiled water with maize meal and pumpkins or butternut, mixed with sugar.

Grace: Wow. That sounds nice. Can you cook it?

Bachelor: Yes, I had a friend from Khayelitsha who taught me. He is at the University of the Witwatersrand now. It's even more popular now, when pumpkins are withering.

Grace: I hope you can teach me too.

Bachelor: And maybe we can catch a live performance at the Jazz Club later this evening? There is one at the City Hall.

Grace: That sounds perfect. I love jazz music.

Bachelor: Me too. It's so smooth and relaxing.

Grace: This is turning out to be a great evening. I'm glad we came here.

Bachelor: Me too. And who knows? Maybe this could be the start of something more than just a friendship.

Grace: *(giggling.)* I was hoping you'd say that. I am truly elated when I am with you.

Bachelor: I'm glad we both feel the same way. Let's make the most of this evening and see where it takes us.

Grace: I couldn't agree more. *(They continued their walk around the harbour, enjoying the sights and each other's company, excited to explore more of Cape Town together.)* Where is everyone?

Bachelor: *(pointing.)* Over there, far head. They must have hastened their walk. But we will reach them and tell them where we are headed: to listen to jazz music live.

Grace: Just the two of us?

Bachelor: Yes. *(They hold hands as they go.)*

Grace: I am enthralled.

Exeunt

7.4.6 Scene Six

(The night has fallen, and the sky is in a deep shade of navy blue. The stars twinkling in the sky, and the moon was casting a soft glow over the ocean. The wind was blowing gently, bringing with it the cool breeze of autumn. Inside the family home, Cynthia and Precious were sitting in the living room. Precious had a sombre expression on her face, and Cynthia could sense that something was still bothering her.)

Cynthia: What's wrong, Precious? You seem upset and intense with anxiety.

Precious: I can't stop thinking about Casanova. Even though he cheated on me with three girls, who knows if there are more? I still love him.

Cynthia: Precious, I know it's hard, but you need to move on. You deserve better than someone who would cheat on you. I have always known that guy is bad news.

Precious: I know, but the love I have for him is anchored in my heart.

Cynthia: I understand, but sometimes love isn't enough. Love must bear the fruits of integrity, honour, comfort, genuineness, fidelity, benediction, alleviation, and elation. You need someone who will treat you right and make you happy.

Precious: I should have listened to him when he warned me about Casanova. He told me he was bad news, but I didn't listen.

Cynthia: You mean Bachelor?

Precious: Yes, him. He warned me about Casanova, but I didn't believe him. Now I regret not listening to him.

Cynthia: I'm sorry, Precious. I shouldn't have pushed you to date Casanova. I was thinking about myself and not what was best for you. But then, it wouldn't have worked either with me dating his friend Charles. I am sorry for pushing you to date Casanova.

Precious: It's not your fault, Cynthia. I made my own decisions. But I appreciate for acknowledging your mistake.

Cynthia: I just want you to be happy, Precious. You deserve to be with someone who will treat you with respect , uprightness and honour.

Precious: I know, and I will try to move on. It won't be easy, but I know I need to do it for myself.

Cynthia: That's the spirit, Precious. And don't worry, I'll be here for you every step of the way. Self love is far more precious than romantic love.

(The two sisters hugged each other, comforted by the love and support they shared for each other. They both knew that moving on from a painful relationship was difficult, but they also knew that they had each other to rely on.)

Exeunt

7.4.7 Scene Seven

(The beach at Hout Bay is quiet and peaceful. The partial altocumulus clouds in the sky cast a slight shadow over the moon and stars; the wind is gentle, along with the cool air; it is the first day of May, and autumn is in full swing.

Casanova is standing alone at the beach, wearing a short, barefoot, and half-naked, outfit with nothing on the upper body. He is lost in his thoughts and deep in sadness, frustration, and hope. His feet are being touched by the waves, and the sound of the ocean is soothing to his ears.)

Casanova: What have I done? I have been such a jerk! All this time, being manipulative and a conniving player, embroiled in conflict with Bachelor for my misdemeanours. How I have lived has been immoral and unacceptable. I should have known better about ramifications of my sexual immorality. What have I gained with all this futility and frivolity? If I were to be honest, neither have I been elated and fulfilled; but persistently chased after wind. I've always been thirsty and yearning for something that shall exhilarate my heart, and I don't know what it is.

(He sighs deeply, and the sound is lost in the waves.)

Casanova: I have dated Rose and Amanda, used them, thereafter; spat them like that. I even never truly loved them, but dumped them for being uncivil, fighting over me in public. That was selfish and unthinkable of me, I was wrong. Whose etiquette and who is shenanigan between me and them?

(He pauses for a moment, looking up at the moon and stars scattered across the deep indigo sky above the altocumulus clouds.)

Casanova: (*sighs deeply, and pounders.*) Then there is Precious and Ntombi.... (*He pauses for a moment.*) Precious is so gentle and calm; she handles situations in mature and gentle like manner-as for Ntombi, she is sweet and prestige but she can become so aggressive. I need to fix things with Precious, but I don't know where to start. After witnessing you-Ntombi, attacking Precious, spilling water on her, and hurling insults, my opinion of you just changed, though my love for Precious had already outweighed the one I have had for you Ntombi. Nevertheless, I'm worse than you, and I have to make this determination to fix my life. Promiscuousness doesn't shine well; promiscuity is dark; neither does it show how manly you're are. What it depicts is foolishness, selfishness, self-indulgence and self-interest. What a waste of time and energy for all my teenage hood! Nothing but frivolity and futility. What have I achieved with all my actions? Heartbreaks!

(*He looks back at the ocean, watching as the waves wash up on the shore.*)

Casanova: Thank you, Bachelor. You've been my rival, but you've also been the only one who's talked some sense into me. You made me see I needed to change my bad behaviour. I hope it's not too late. (*Casanova closes his eyes, taking a deep breath of the ocean air.*)

Casanova: I have a lot of work to do. I am determined to make things right this time, so help me, Christ Jesus, cleanse my heart and renew my mind. (*As he stands there, the wind and breeze blowing, he feels a glimmer of hope that things could still work out with Precious.*)

(***Continues***.): Oh, how small I am, a mere speck in the vastness of existence. I once believed I could conquer the world, possess it all for myself. But now, as I gaze upon the ocean's endless expanse, I realize the futility of my pursuits.

(*Taking a deep mesmerising breath.*): The ocean, stretching far beyond the horizon, whispers tales of ancient depths and uncharted territories. Its waves, crashing against the shore, remind me of the power and majesty that lie beyond my grasp. How can I, a mere mortal, compete with such grandeur? (*He gazes up the heavens.*)

Casanova: And if the ocean alone humbles me, what of the 100k light year Milky Way galaxy, with its swirling stars and infinite mysteries? It stretches across the night sky, reminding me of the countless worlds and possibilities that exist beyond my comprehension.

(*The stars and moon send* **a** *glowing lights through* **the** *altocumulus clouds scattered across atmosphere.*)

Casanova: (*looking straight up the starry heavens.*) Yet even the Milky Way is but a tiny fragment in the vast universe, spanning 93 billion light-years. It is a cosmic tapestry, woven with celestial wonders that defy my understanding. How can I, with my limited reach, claim dominion over such immense beauty?

(*Displeased.*): In my pursuit of pleasure and conquest, I neglected to see the grandeur that lies beyond my desires. I am but a fleeting soul, destined to fade into the vastness of time. I must learn to embrace the humility that comes with acknowledging my place in this wondrous universe. (*he looks around, stares at the ocean.*)

For I am not meant to possess the whole world, nor can I ever truly grasp its infinite wonders. Instead, I shall strive to find meaning within myself, to appreciate the fleeting moments of joy and connection that life presents.

(*Amazed and Hopeful*): Oh, how small I am, and yet, how fortunate to exist amidst such cosmic splendour. May my regrets transform into a deeper understanding of my place in this vast, magnificent universe.

Casanova: (*sighs.*) I need to make amends for my past misdemeanours and the futile lifestyle I have lived. Hopefully, I win her heart again as I have fractured it with my lies and deceit, because I could not control my lust.

Exit

7.4.8 Scene Eight

(Bachelor stands on the dock, looking out at the ocean. The moon and stars shine brightly above him, casting a slight shadow over the beach. The wind blows gently, bringing a cool breeze along with it. Ships pass by all the way to the commercial harbour in Table Bay, Cape Town. Bachelor begins to speak.)

Bachelor: *(Inhaling and exhaling the cool breeze from the sea.)* As the waves crash below me, I can't help but feel the weight of the world lift off my shoulders. It's been a long road to get here-standing on this dock, watching the moon and stars across the starry heavens, glowing and glittering above me, with dancing altocumulus clouds scattered across the stratosphere. The peacefulness of this beach is just what I need, a moment to collect my thoughts and reflect on the journey that has led me to this point.

(He gazes at the heavens, sees glowing moon and stars above the altocumulus clouds, then gaze upon the ocean.)

Bachelor: *(to himself.)* As I stand here, looking out at the ocean, I can't help but feel a sense of peace. The world is so vast, so limitless, and yet, I've always felt so small. So insignificant. But these ships passing by remind me that there is more to this world than I could ever imagine.

Bachelor: *(gazing at the raging waves, then afar below the horizon across the ocean.)* The ocean, stretching far and wide, Is but a reflection of the vastness of my heart when it beats for my beloved. Its currents, gentle yet fierce, carry the echoes of our shared laughter and whispered promises. In its ebb and flow, I find solace, knowing that our love is as eternal as the tides. I love you Grace. (*He lifts up his head, gazes up the sky through the altocumulus clouds scattered across the atmosphere.*)

(**Continues**):But beyond the ocean lies the Milky Way galaxy, a cosmic tapestry of stars and mysteries. Just as its countless constellations illuminate the night sky, my love for you illuminates my very being. O Grace, you've captivated my heart!

(Bachelor looks up at the moon and stars, taking a deep breath.)

Bachelor: *(to himself.)* I used to be so consumed with self-doubt and insecurity. I thought I had to be a certain way to fit in, to be accepted. But now, I know that's not true. I don't have to put on a facade to please others. I can be who I am, sensitive and all, and that's what makes me strong.

(Bachelor looks out at the ocean, listening to the waves crash below him and watching the ships pass by.)

Bachelor: *(reflecting.)* Since I reached my teenage hood, I couldn't be firm and bold but felt so low; thinking I had to fit into a mould of what society deemed as masculine. I shall do that no more, and that's thanks to the support of some incredible people in my life I've met, but also; having learnt Casanova's futile and frivolous lifestyle bringing nothing but trouble and weariness.

(he pause for a moment, stares ta ships passing bay, listening to raging waves, gazing far across the horizon.)

Bachelor: *(at ease.)* Casanova used to be my rival. He has lived his life like a player, always playing around with girls. But I know that's not the way I want to live. His wild and carefree lifestyle may have taught him some valuable lessons, with the hope that he comes to his senses: as for that; I want to find love in a way that feels natural and real, not by playing games or manipulating others. I no longer hold any grudges against him. I hope he changes his ways and finds what he's looking for.

(Bachelor takes another deep breath, feeling the wind blowing through his hair.)

Bachelor: *(appeased.)* I'm grateful for the people who have helped me along the way. Sithabile and Matthew showed me that it's okay to be myself, which I don't have to conform to anyone else's standards. And Grace... just the thought of her makes my heart skip a beat. I don't know what the future holds for us, but I'm excited to find out. We have just spent the evening together, listening to jazz and walking through the city. It was like nothing else mattered except the moment we were in. I feel hopeful that things may work out between us, and I'm excited to see where our connection leads.

(Bachelor looks out at the ocean, feeling a sense of hope and possibility.)

Bachelor: *(Sighs.)* As the wind blows through my hair and the cool air fills my lungs, I know that I'm exactly where I'm meant to be. I'm a better person than I was before, and I'm grateful for the people who have helped me along the way. Autumn is now in full in full swing, but for me, it's a new beginning. A chance to embrace who I am and what I want out of life. And with Grace by my side, I know that anything is possible. Let me call it a night, my brother must be wondering and worried where am I.

(Bachelor takes one last deep breath, then turns and walks away from the dock, watching as the ships pass by on their way to the commercial harbour in Table Bay, Cape Town.)

Exit

7.4.9 Scene Nine

(It late night around 11:00 p.m. Green Point, a family home mansion, the cool breeze is blowing, altocumulus scattered across the sky, enter Valentine and Sharon.)

Valentine: Have you seen Bachelor today?

Sharon: No, I have not. When last did you see him?

Valentine: He had taken some days off, since they summoned him to do some TV show I have not seen since yesterday. I am worried.

Sharon: "I am sure he is fine." Wherever he is, he is a big boy; tall and athletic.

Valentine: Hopefully.

Sharon: So how did it go with the prisoner?

Valentine: *(in fear.)* Hey, there's something profound that the prisoner is not telling me.

Sharon: *(Curious.)* What is it? What did he say?

Valentine: He does not want to reveal any other name to be involved in my parents' murder. But he mentioned a woman by the name of Delilah Osmond, who worked at the Vredehoek Orphanage Centre. He said if I want more information about the lost twin and everything else, I should go ask her.

Sharon: Isn't that the same woman you went to see in Simon's Town?

Valentine: I think it is, though I have not yet gotten her surname.

Sharon: Visit her again.

Valentine: No, it will alert her that I am up to something.

Sharon: What else did the prisoner say?

Valentine: He said he dropped the infant at the Vredehoek Orphanage. This is so contradictory to his original statement.

Sharon: Why did he lie about the whereabouts of the baby?

Valentine: Maybe he did not want heavier punishment than he got with his friend. I think I should go to Vredehoek tomorrow, find information in that centre. I want to have solid information before I tell Bachelor the truth and find out if Casanova is truly our brother. *(In an instant, Bachelor arrives.)* Bachelor, where have you been? I have been sickly worried about you.

Bachelor: *(Sleepy)*. I am sorry; I went out with some friends and thereafter went to the City Hall to listen to some jazz concerts.

Valentine: You are coming from the CBD?

Bachelor: Yes.

Valentine: Please report when you tell us the time you are going to return.

Bachelor: I will, but I am grown up, on the doorstep of adulthood, I can take care of myself.

Valentine: You'll always be my little brother, no matter what; I have strong instinct to be protective of you .

Bachelor: *(drowsy.)* I know, I couldn't be more grateful for that. Goodnight. *(He takes some few steps climbing the staircase and pauses, looking back.) Why* are you still awake, at this time of the night?

Valentine: *(nervous.)* We were just worried about you.

Bachelor: Okay, cool, thanks. *(He climbs the stairs, then stops.)* Valentine, where is my toothbrush? I looked for it everywhere, and I never took it out of my bathroom.

Valentine: *(nervously.)* I don't know; maybe you misplaced it.

Bachelor: I don't know. I even had to get a new one this morning.

Valentine: At least you now have it. Are you not hungry? I bought some pizzas from Debonairs-the best pizza Franchise in the country.

Bachelor: No, I am not, I'll go take a nap. Goodnight *(he goes.)*

Valentine: Hmm, I love him so much; I'm very protective of him.

Sharon: As you should. I pray for all things to turn out well.

Valentine: Thank you, honey. *(They embrace.)* I love you so much.

Sharon: I love you too. *(They kiss.)*

Exeunt

7.4.10 Scene Ten

(Fish Hoek, mid-morning, a restaurant where Cynthia and Charles sit; They adorn the surroundings with beautiful blooms, trees, and roses, which have turned yellow, reddish, and orange, and leaves withering on the ground. The vegetation has lost its vibrant green colour, transitioning into warm shades of red, orange, and yellow.
The gentle breeze rustled the leaves vibrant green colour, as it transitioned into warm shades of red, orange, and yellow. The gentle breeze rustled the leaves and petals, creating a peaceful ambiance.)

Charles: *(Turning to Cynthia.)* Hey, isn't it mesmerising to gaze at the ocean from here?

Cynthia: *(Smiling.)* Yes, it's breath-taking. The ocean always brings a sense of calmness to me. *(The breeze from the Atlantic Ocean is cooling off.)*

Charles: *(Takes a sip of his coffee and lets out a deep sigh.)* You know, I' am infuriated with my dad. He cheated on my mom, with his infidelity with Marry. I can't 'believe his treacherousness to our family.

Cynthia: *(She senses some hurt in Charles's voice.)* O Sorry. *(Avoiding eye contact).*

Charles: Wait? Did you know about this?

Cynthia: *(face softened.)* I know this is hard for you, Charles, but I have to tell you something. I've known about your dad's affair for a while now.

Charles: *(Eyes widen.)* What? How come you didn't tell me? You're my girlfriend. I thought we were supposed to share everything.

(In a distance, the Atlantic Ocean shimmered under the mid-morning sun, adding to the natural beauty of Fish Hoek, Cape Town, South Africa. The sky is adorned with cirrus clouds, which created a soft, white veil across the sky, adding to the overall calmness of the scene.)

Cynthia: *(putting down the fork.)* I didn't know how to tell you, Charles. I didn't want to hurt you, but I didn't want to keep it a secret from you. But I told him he must confess to you.

Charles: I can't believe it. You lied to me. Who else knows this?

Cynthia: Bachelor also knows it. We thought it would devastate you if you heard it from us, and you would not believe us.

Charles: *(leaning back on the chair.)* I appreciate you being honest with me now, but I'm just not sure how to handle this situation. It's like everything is falling apart.

Cynthia: *(reaching across the table and taking Charles's hand.)* I'm here for you, Charles. We'll get through this together. I know it's tough, but we have to be strong for your mom and your family. Have you spoken to your dad about it?

Charles: Yes, I have. I can see and sense he is deeply sorry. But I feel like we cannot sweep it under the carpet and not tell my mother the truth.

Cynthia: Give him time, but it must not be late. The truth has a way of coming out. How did you even find out?

Charles: I was arguing with Casanova about his bad behaviour and he exposed my dad.

Cynthia: That dragon! He even hurt my sister.

Charles: I think he has been one, but I believe he has learnt a lesson.

Cynthia: What lesson? That guy will always be a manipulator.

Charles: Let's not get into Casanova now, otherwise, it shall ruin our morning. I just want your comfort in all of this. This has grieved my heart.

Cynthia: *(Cynthia squeezed Charles's hand.)* Of course, Charles. I'll always be here for you. I am sorry for not telling the truth.

(As they continued their meal, the cirrus clouds across the sky started to dissipate, allowing the sun to shine brightly on the beautiful scenery around them. The couple sat in silence, lost in their thoughts, but comforted by each other's presence.)

Charles: It's okay. Who would believe a girlfriend telling him about his father's infidelity? Any guy would be outraged. I'm sorry, Cynthia. I should have been more understanding. Thank you for being honest with me.

Cynthia: *(smiles.)* You don't have to apologize, Charles. I just want to support you in any way I can.

(The couple sits in silence, enjoying the beauty of the surrounding scenery. The warm shades of the vegetation added to the romantic ambience of the restaurant, while the cirrus clouds above them created a peaceful atmosphere.)

Charles: I love you so much; you arouse my flesh and soul.

(Cynthia and Charles held hands, knowing that they would face whatever challenges come their way together.)

Cynthia: I love you more. You are my pillar of strength. *(They kiss.)*

Charles: My mother is back, by the way.

Cynthia: *(Elated.)* Really?

Charles: You must thrill indeed.

Charles: Yes, I am

Exeunt

7.4.11 Scene Eleven
(Fish Hoek, in late morning, the sun shines across the sky; the Atlantic Ocean shimmers under the late-morning sun. Enter Mrs Andrews in a coffee shop at unease and frustration.)

MRS ANDREWS: I cannot believe he did that to me! How could he? He has destroyed my trust. I cannot trust him anymore; it is even worse: I found out about this through his student whispering behind my back. I am pissed.

(She looks around, stares at the ocean from afar, and freezes.)

Mrs Andrews: (Sighs.) Maybe it's my fault, I have been away for a long time; we have been so disconnected, even our son noticed this. But we did nothing.

(Putting down the fork, leaning back on the chair.)

Mrs Andrews: What I am wrathful for is that everyone seems to know it, including my son. But what could he have done? I cannot blame him.

(Uneased and frustrated, she puts her arms on the table and her head between them.)

Mrs Andrews: Could this be the end of our marriage, our home that we've been working on for 30 years?

(She sits up straight, with her hands on her lap.)

If we had issues, why did he not speak to me and be open about it? He pursued what was expedient and not what was meaningful; he pursued his pleasure at the expense of our trust. *(In an instance, Paul arrives, noticing Mrs. Andrews in deep thought.)*

Paul: Good morning, Portia.

(Portia is silent, in deep thought; Paul sits in front of her across the table.)

Paul: "Morning Portia."

Mrs Andrews: Hi. *(Rolling eyes.)*

Paul: (*curious*) What is wrong? You don't look like yourself, and seem to be in deep thought.

Mrs Andrews: (*sipping a coffee, gazing away, then looking back at Paul and frowning.*) As if you do not know, I can't believe you!

Paul: I am so sorry; I can understand your heart is in an extinguished state.

Mrs Andrews: You knew all of this? And you did not tell me?

Paul: John is my friend; it was not my place to tell.

Mrs Andrews: (*Harsh voice.*) So, you approve of his infidelity?

Paul: No, not at all. I strongly condemn what he has done to put his marriage in jeopardy.

Mrs Andrews: Well, it is, I do not even know what to do, how to even look at Andres now.

Paul: I get your frustration and wrath, but please take your time. Just do not forsake the marriage you have built for three decades.

Mrs Andrews: (*Sighs.*) I am sorry for taking my frustrations out on you. John Andrews is at fault here. But then, do you men reprimand each other if one of you does something wrong?

Paul: Yes, we do. I told him to end things.

Mrs Andrews: (*Unpleased.*) Well, he did it after he had already been caught. Would he have ended them if Cynthia had not? Or had my son not confronted him? It took my drunken son to confront him.

Paul: Let's not do any speculation now, but what I know is that he is deeply sorry. I have never seen him in such a state. Please do not give up on him for some foolish, silly mistake. I do not think he deliberately wanted to hurt you.

Mrs Andrews: (*sighs.*) I hear you. ***Exeunt***

7.4.12 Scene Twelve

(In the mid-afternoon, the orphanage centre in Vredehoek, South Africa, surrounded by trees and the fallen leaves of autumn, painted the ground. The air is cool and crisp, and the sun is setting in the sky, casting a warm orange glow over the centre.
Valentine approaches the entrance of the centre, feeling both anxious and hopeful.
As he enters the building, a friendly caretaker, a woman with kind eyes and a gentle smile, greets him. She introduced herself as Mrs. Petersen and offered to show him around.)

Mrs Peterson: How can I help you, sir?

Valentine: I am looking for some information. On the 15th of June 1992, we were invaded in our home, and my parents were murdered.

Mrs Peterson: *(sad.)* Wow, that's so sad. I am so sorry. What happened?

Valentine: There were two infants, both three months old, and one got kidnapped. I went to visit the culprit in prison. He said he dropped him here on June 15, 1992. It was late in the evening and dark.

Mrs Peterson: Ah, yes, I remember that day well. It was a sad day for us all. They left the poor little thing on our doorstep with nothing but a note attached to his blanket. We named him Michael.

Valentine: *(heart sinks as he hears the story.)* Is there any information you might have about the child's birth parents or if he had been adopted?

Mrs Peterson: We tried to find the parents, but unfortunately, we had no luck. As for adoption, Michael was adopted, but they did not do it through legal channels. We suspect a private adoption agency took him.

Valentine: *(eyes widening in shock and aggrieved.)* Is there any way to find out who had adopted Michael?

Mrs Peterson: We have some information. *(She is rummaging through a drawer in her desk.)* Here are some photos of Michael when he first arrived and when he was a year old.

Valentine: (taking *the photos and examining them closely, he feels a lump forming in his throat as he looks at the innocent face of the baby.)* Thank you.

(Says softly, trying to keep his emotions in check.): Is there anything else you can tell me?

Mrs Petersen: *(hesitated for a moment before speaking again.)* There was a woman who worked here by the name of Delilah Osmond. She was one of our caregivers, but she was fired and arrested for selling a toddler in the spring of 1993.

Valentine: *(eyes widening in shock.)* Do you know where she is now?

Mrs Peterson: Yes, she was apprehended and served five years in prison. As for her whereabouts now, she lives in Simon's Town with a daughter named Leah.

Valentine: *(Feels a sense of urgency.)* Thank you very much. I suspect Michael might be my brother.

Mrs Peterson: *(saddened.)* O? I hope you find him.

Valentine: Can I take a picture of him?

Mrs Peterson: Yes, sure.

Valentine: Thanks. *(He takes out his Apple iPad and takes a picture.)* Thank you very much. I will keep in touch.

Mrs Peterson: pleasure *(They shake hands.)* I am thrilled to help.

Exeunt

7.4.13 Scene Thirteen

(Fish Hoek, a suburban street lined with houses of varying architecture from the 20th and 21st centuries, each with its unique charm. The trees, with leaves of autumn hues and roses in full bloom added a touch of natural beauty to the street. Altocumulus clouds dotted the sky, casting shadows on the pavement in the late afternoon light of Cynthia and Precious walking down the street together.)

Cynthia: Yes, I am telling you; we have fixed things with Charles. I am so thrilled this is all over.

Precious: *(Weak smile.)* I am happy for you.

Cynthia: *(notices Precious' unease mood, seemed to be lost in thought and appeared to be stressed.)*

Cynthia: I am sorry my little sister, for Casanova to hurt like that. I shouldn't have gloated about my relationship with Charles so soon.

Precious: *(Heavy sighs.)* I don't know what to do.

Cynthia: *(puts a comforting arm around her sister's shoulders.)* I'm so sorry, Precious. You don't deserve to be treated like that.

(Just then, a Mercedes Benz car pulled up next to them, and the driver rolled down the window. It is Casanova.)

Casanova: *(Looking at Precious with pleading eyes.)* Hey, baby. Precious, can we talk?

Cynthia: *(stepping in front of her sister, protectively.)* You teared her heart Casanova. She doesn't want to talk to you.

Casanova: *(Face falls, looks genuinely remorseful.)* I know I messed up, and I'm sorry. Please, can I just talk to her privately?

(After a moment of hesitation, Precious nodded.)

Precious: Okay, Cynthia. I'll talk to him alone.

(Cynthia gives Precious a supportive squeeze on the shoulder before walking away to give them some privacy.)

Casanova: *(apologetic voice.)* I'm sorry, Precious. I messed up big time. I should have been honest with you from the start. I never should have lied to you and cheated on you.

Precious: *(She looks into his eyes, and sees the pain and remorsefulness all over his face.)*

Precious: *(softy.)* I need time to process this, Casanova. I don't know if I can forgive you just yet.

Casanova: *(Nodding.)* I understand. I'll do whatever it takes to make it right. I just hope you can find it in your heart to forgive me.

(Precious says nothing in response. She simply walks away, leaving Casanova to reflect on his mistakes and hope that one day she can forgive him.)

Exeunt

7.4.14 Scene Fourteen

(The sun begins to dip below the horizon. Bachelor gets ready for his date with Grace. He stands in his room overlooking the Atlantic Ocean, admiring the view as he prepares himself. It's late autumn, and the altocumulus clouds in the sky cast a warm orange glow over the city.

Bachelor checks himself out in the mirror, dressed in a black blazer and white button-up shirt. The black blazer symbolizes his suave demeanour, while the white shirt represents his pure intentions towards Grace. He pairs the outfit with dark blue jeans and black dress shoes, completing the look with a silver watch.

Bachelor is nervous, but excited about the evening ahead. He met Grace during a soccer match and knew instantly that he wanted to ask her out. The warm autumn air adds to his excitement, knowing that this evening will be unforgettable.

With one last look in the mirror, Bachelor heads out of his apartment and towards the restaurant where he is meeting Grace. The crisp autumn air greets him as he steps outside, and he takes a deep breath, ready to make this evening one to remember.)

Bachelor: *(apprehensive.)* I feel a bit of hysteria and I am highly strung. What if I mess up or say something stupid?

(Takes a deep breath and calms his edginess.)

Bachelor: (Anticipation.) This is it now; it is now, or never. I have come so far, I feel so good and beautiful. I may be nervous...

(Sighs and fixes hair; stands in front of the mirror. cannot contain his excitement.)

Bachelor: But I feel like I am on top of the world, entailed with feverishness. I have come so far to overcome my fear and

introversion. Had I not met Sithabile and Matthew I do not know...
I have such courage today and so enthralled for the date I have with
Grace in town.

(Agitated and Courageous.)

Bachelor: Casanova truly made me feel so negative about myself.
I had low self–esteem, moreover; I believe I brought some sense
in him and shall never look down upon me, neither shall I feel
negatively about myself.

*(He takes a deep breath, gazes out the window, and feels a cooling
breeze of the cold bunguela current from the Atlantic Ocean.)*

Bachelor: I feel like the world is much bigger than I have ever
thought, and just a small puzzle in it, moreover; tonight, is my night,
and I couldn't be happier.

*(He stands in his bedroom overlooking the sea, admiring the ships
passing by, and the altocumulus clouds in the heavens scattered with
stars, casting a warm orange glow.)*

Bachelor: I am exhilarated for this date, ready to show Grace
the best night of her life and have such a stimulating and titillating
evening.

(Enthrallment and eagerness.)

Bachelor: I can feel it, this evening shall end well tonight, with
Grace by my side, complimenting each other. I feel a sense of purpose
and animation.

*(While Bachelor is in his bedroom preparing for a date, Valentine
arrives in the lounge.)*

Valentine: Now I have the truth. I feel I am going to find him.
Casanova has to be Michael, who was adopted from that orphanage
centre. I could feel these two women were lying to me about
something. *(Doorbell bell rings.)* Come in. *(A Gate Keeper enters with
an envelope.)*

Gate-Keeper: Here is the letter for you, sir. They dropped it
today.

Valentine: Where is it from?

Gate-Keeper: I am not sure, but it seems like it's from the hospital. (*Giving him the envelope.*)

Valentine: (*heart pumping* harder.) Thank you. Have a nice evening, you can go home now.

Gate-Keeper: Goodnight. (*The gatekeeper leaves.*)

Valentine: (*opening and reading the letter.*) The moment of truth has come.

(*The sun sets on a cool autumn evening in Green Point, Cape Town, and the sky is painted with shades of purple, orange, and pink. A majestic mansion stands tall on a hill overlooking the city. The mansion is surrounded by lush gardens, filled with flowers and trees, turning yellow, orange, and red, rustling in the cool breeze.*)

Valentine: I have antedated for this day for a long time; o God, let it be true.

(*Eagerness and distressfulness.*)

Valentine: Could they indeed be twins? What do I do now if they're not?

(*Valentine sits in the lounge on the couch, holding an envelope in his hands. He takes a deep breath, his heart racing as he opens the envelope and dreads the DNA results, he had requested.*)

Valentine: (*shocked and shivering.*) My goodness, he is truly my brother. (*Weeps.*) My God! 99.99%

(*He recalls the day his parents were murdered, while he was in the kitchen with Bachelor and Matthew-now Casanova, with his parents outside.*)

Valentine: Casanova is indeed Bachelor's twin. I am glad; I have got joy; deep in my heart, up in my mind; down in my feet-that I have finally found you, brother. Praise be the Almighty; Hallelujah!

(*His heart sinks, and his body shudders with a mix of emotions—shock, sadness, and excitement.*)

Valentine: Helen, you are going to pay for this, you and your friend Delilah.

(He leaves the DNA result on the table and rushes out of the mansion, getting into his car)

Valentine: *(frustrated and distressed.)* Let me go to Hout Bay right now!

Exit

(Bachelor comes down from upstairs; already dressed for his date and excited.)

Bachelor: Valentine! *(Calling him.)* I just heard him arrive about 15 minutes ago. *(Confused.)* Where is?

(He calls out loud, but gets no response, he paces around.)

Bachelor: Let me look for my electromagnetic proton converter here; I can't find it in my bedroom, and my battery is almost dead. *(He goes around the lounge and spots it on the* table.) Thank goodness, here it is.

(As he takes it, he spots the same DNA result laying on the table.)

Bachelor: *(wondering.)* What in the hell is this?

(Sits alone in the lounge room, holding a piece of paper with the DNA results. It's dusk outside, and the room is dimly lit by a lamp on his desk. We can see altocumulus clouds through the window, slowly gathering across the darkened navy heavens. He looks visibly shaken and speaks to himself.)

Bachelor :*(He is shocked, shivering and shuttering.)* I can't believe this. This paper in my hand proves that Casanova and I are twins. Twins! And I did not know. How could Valentine keep something like this from me? I thought I knew everything about my family history.

(He pauses, taking a deep breath, as the cool autumn breeze blows through the window of the lounge Bachelor sits in disbelief, staring at the DNA results in his hand. It confirms that he and Casanova are twins with a 99.99% probability.)

Bachelor: (*crying.*) They murdered my parents when I was just an infant. I've always known that. But to find out now that I have a twin brother, and that he's been living with me all this time... I don't know... I am shivering; this is such an unbearable affliction.

(He stands up and paces the room.)

Bachelor: Casanova and I have always had our differences. We fought a lot in high school. But now, looking back, it all makes sense. We're brothers. And I never even knew it, all this time we've not been aware .

(He sits back down, holding the DNA results.)

Bachelor: But why did Valentine keep this from me? And why did he split us up? Did he think it would be better for us to grow up apart? I don't understand.

(He asks aloud, his voice trembling with emotion.)

Bachelor: Why didn't he tell me? How could he keep such a huge secret from me?

(He takes a deep breath and looks out the window.)

Bachelor: I can't believe it! (*He shakes his head in disbelief.*) All those fights, all those arguments, and we were brothers all along. It's insane.

(Thinking in deep thought, appeased and displeased.)

Bachelor: But one thing for sure, I'm glad that we resolved our differences before I found out the truth. It would have been a shame to waste all these years hating each other, only to find out we're family.

(He looks back at the DNA results.)

Bachelor: These changes everything. I have a brother. A twin brother. And I **know nothing** about him. I need to talk to Casanova. I need to know everything.

(He stands up and walks to the door.)

Bachelor: I had thought of him as a rival, and we had quarrelled most of the time. Our relationship has been full of intricacies because we are brothers without even knowing it.

(He's filled with a sense of longing and sadness. He comes back to the lounge, leaving the door open, and paces around the room in distress and frustration.)

Bachelor: But first, I need to process all of this. I need time to reflect on this...

(As the altocumulus clouds outside darken with the setting sun, Bachelor shivers, both from the cold breeze and the shock of the news.)

Bachelor: *(Sitting on the couch.)* I can't believe that my 33-year-old brother Valentine has hidden this from me for so long. I feel so betrayed, hurt, and confused. Let me go find him. I need to find my twin brother. *(He goes upstairs, takes his car keys, comes back downstairs, takes the DNA result with him, shuts the door, and drives away.)*

Exit

7.4.15 Scene Fifteen

(As you enter Helen's hotel in Hout Bay, the warm glow of the reception desk greets you, casting a comforting light on the polished wooden floors. The air is crisp and cool, typical of late autumn evenings in this part of the world. The sound of a crackling fireplace wafts through the air, making you feel instantly at home. At the reception, Sylvia enters, busy with a call and Pretty cleaning some tables, couches, and chairs.)

Valentine: *(Rushing in deep anger and frustration.)* Helen! Helen! I am looking for Helen!

Sylvia: *(Drops the call, Valentine rushes to her.)* Hello! How can I help you?

Valentine: *(in a high-pitched voice.)* I am looking for Helen!

Sylvia: You need to book to see her. I can't just let you see her. *(Pretty stands still in shock.)*

Valentine: Where is she? Let me go to her office. *(He goes, Sylvia tries to stop him, but he goes, and then Helen comes out in shock and lets him inside her office.)*

Pretty: *(coming towards Sylvia at the reception desk.)* What is going on? Is this not the same guy who came here last month?

Sylvia: *(wondering.)* I don't know, I don't know.

Pretty: Let me go listen.

Sylvia: No. Look, here comes Casanova from outside. What shall he say, seeing you snooping in her mother's office like that?

(Inside Helen's office, Valentine storms in, his face twisted with anger.)

Valentine: How could you do this to me? How could you hide the truth from me for all these years? You hid the truth from my entire family.

Helen: *(looking up at him with a calm face but her eyes betraying her nerves.)*

Helen*: (Evenly.)* I'm not sure what you're talking about, Valentine.

Valentine: *(with narrowed eyes.)* Don't play dumb with me. I know you've been hiding the fact that you have been hiding my brother all this time, Bachelor's twin, and that you adopted him from the Vredehoek Orphanage Centre with the help of Delilah.

(Helen's mouth opened, then closed.)

Helen *:(Voice faltering.)* I don't know what to say.

Valentine: I left the hard copy of the DNA, but luckily, I have the soft copy in my email as well.

(He takes out his Apple iPad tablet and shows her the DNA test that proves Bachelor and Casanova are twins, and both of them are my younger brothers.)

Valentine: Are you still denying it? And even that you adopted him in a dodgy way?

Helen: *(Voice shaking.)* I didn't know at first that Casanova was Bachelor's twin. I didn't find out until a few years after I adopted him.

Valentine*: (eyes filled with tears.)* And you never thought to tell me? To let me meet my brother? To let him meet his twin brother, Bachelor?

Helen: *(reaches out a hand, but Valentine jerks away from her touch.)* I'm sorry, Valentine. I didn't know what to do. I was scared. I didn't want to hurt you.

(At that moment, the door burst open and Casanova strode in, his face a mask of shock.)

Casanova: *(demanding.)* What's going on?

Valentine: *(Face full of sadness.)* Casanova, we're brothers.

Casanova: *(eyes widen.)* What? How is that possible?

Valentine: Years ago, on the 21st of March 1992, my parents were blessed with twins—brotherly twins. I was 15 years. It was in autumn. (He takes a breath.)

(Continues): On June 15, 1992 *(Weeping)*, our home, back in Green Point, was invaded, and those thugs murdered my parents. They took nothing. I was in the kitchen with Bachelor, the other twin, while the other one, Matthew, was outside in the evening with my parents. They murdered them and took the other twin with them. They were apprehended, but never really told the truth. We never found out what happened since then.

Casanova: *(aggrieved.)* How do you know I am the twin? Mom? *(Helen is in tears.)*

Valentine: Years passed until now. I have been hearing that Bachelor resembles some guy called Casanova, with whom he went to Fish Hoek High School.

Casanova: *(In agreement and sadness.)* People always say that.

Valentine: I have been doing some digging recently. I went to my uncle. She told me about Helen adopting a child a year after you went missing and about a woman named Delilah. I went to prison to see the killer of our parents. He said he dropped the child off at Vredehoek Orphanage centre on June 15, 1992, the same day, same year, and same night our parents were murdered. The caregiver there told me they left you with no trace. And they named you Michael. But you were adopted in a dodgy way, through a woman by the name of Delilah, who now lives in Simon's Town. She was fired and arrested for selling a toddler and served five years.

Casanova: *(In tears).* Mother, is this true? Was I adopted from Vredehoek?

Helen: (*crying and shivering.*) Yes, honey, you were. I did not know at first that you were Valentine's brother. I found out a few years later. Delilah deceived me.

Casanova: How do you know about Valentine?

Helen: (*Shivering.*) Her mother, Bridget Johnson Green, and she started this hotel together back in the mid-80s. We were in a partnership.

Casanova: (*devastated and inflicted.*)

Helen: (*afflicted.*) I was scared. I was afraid I was going to be implicated in your parent's murder.

Valentine: (*Shouting.*) Are you not now? Soon after our parents died, you shut us off from this hotel. Who murdered our parents? Why did you keep quiet all this time?

Helen: (*crying.*) I don't know. Delilah has been blackmailing me about that and even said we should plot to sabotage your relationship with Sharon.

Valentine*: (Intense.)* what?

Helen: I think Delilah murdered your parents. Revisit that prisoner.

Casanova: What about you, mom? You illegally adopted me. What about your crimes?

Helen: I am so sorry.

Casanova: How will this fix things? Do you know how much we hated and sabotaged each other with Bachelor? It was not until recently, in April; that we began to be civil with each other.

Valentine: I am so sorry.

Casanova: Does Bachelor know if I exist? Has he ever wanted to find me?

Valentine: No. He does not even know he has a twin. We hid it from him. Our family thought it would cripple him more to know that not only did he lose parents he never saw but lost his twin too-do not even know it alive or dead.

Casanova: *(In tears, afflicted with grievousness and infliction.)* This is too heavy. Can I see the DNA results?

(Valentine shows him.) My God, I can't believe I have been quarrelling with my twin brother all this time. (He goes.)

Helen and Valentine: Where are you going?

Casanova: To find him.

Valentine: I can take you.

Casanova: No, I shall find him myself. You two are full of lies.

Exit

Valentine: Helen, this is all your fault.

Helen: I am sorry.

Valentine: You know what to do, Helen. *(Valentine goes, Helen is left shivering, crying and inflicted).*

Exeunt

7.5 Act Five

7.5.1 Scene One

(It is 10:00 p.m. In Cape Town CBD. Beautiful and vibrant, full of energy and activity; the streets lined up with crystal lit buildings and bustling restaurants, café and bars. The city's stunning Dutch, Gothic, Georgian-Victorian and the streetlights and colourful neon signs illuminate modern architecture.

The weather is gloomy, with a sky overcast by the stratocumulus clouds low-lying, appearing in large rounded masses about to bring drizzle and rain as they are thick and dark. You can feel the cooling moist moisture FROM Atlantic Ocean in one's body; with the prevailing winds from the south, brining moist air from the ocean, exacerbating the stratocumulus clouds.

Enter Grace, sitting alone on a table in a restaurant by the Cape Town City Hall. The City Hall is an Edwardian architectural style, stands tall and grand in the heart of the CBD; with its towering clock that can be seen from kilometres around; beautifully illuminated, adding to the city's enchantment and mesmerisation)

Grace: *(She sits alone on a table, staring at the phone as the watch ticks on. She looks around at the sound of the opening door, hoping to see Bachelor, but other couples coming in).*

Grace :(Asking herself.) Where is he? It has been three hours. Has he forgotten? Has he changed his mind?

(Shakes her head, trying to clear negative thoughts.)

Grace: No, he would not do that. After all the fun and enjoyment, we have had, he ditches me like this? Perhaps he is just running late. Something must have come up.

(Checking her phone again, with no messages or missed calls neither text on Facebook and Mix-it.)

Grace: Why has he not called? Why has he not even sent a text to alert me what's keeping him up?

(She puts her head in her hands, puts it on the table, leans back on the chair, feeling tears welling up.)

Grace: I was so elated and enthralled by this date, for us to spend more time together, and now it feels like he is not interested in me. *(She grabs a young, handsome waiter in his early 20s passing by.)* Am I beautiful?

Waiter: *(Confused.)* What's wrong?

Grace: Is there something wrong with my countenance? Am I ugly?

Waiter: No, you are exquisite with your Nordic features; the hair, nose, eyes and chicks.

Grace: (frustrated.) Why has he ditched me up then? Why has he stood me up?

Waiter: Maybe something came up. Go home now. You have been here for hours. If he does not, in the following days, you shall know he is not meant for you. Sorry I have to serve those couples. (He goes.)

(Grace looks at a happy couple, then at two gay couples in front of her. She feels afflicted as she looks around.)

Grace: I am so hurt, and never been afflicted like this.

(Candies walk into the restaurant and spotting Grace sitting alone.)

Candies: Grace! Oh, my goodness, I am so sorry I am late. I got stuck in traffic.

Grace: *(Forcing a smile.)* It's okay Candies. I am just glad you are here.

Candies: *(Sitting down across from her.)* How is it going? Where is Bachelor?

Grace: *(Smile fading.)* He is not here. I have been waiting for three hours.

Candies :(*Surprised.)* What? Three hours? Has he called or texted or anything?

Grace: No, no calls, texts or messages. Absolutely nothing.

Candies: *(concerned.)* It is unlike him. He seemed so sweet and genuine. Something must have come up.

Grace: *(Arising frustration.)* But why has he not called? Why hasn't he alerted me about what is going on?

Candies: *(Comforting her.)* Maybe he couldn't, maybe is in some trouble or anything. You know there is chaos and unprecedentedness in this world. Some things happen beyond our measure and control.

Grace :(*Tears welling up.*) I feel such a fool, like I am not even worth a phone call.

Candies: *(firmly.)* No, Grace, don't you dare think that. You are worth everything. Bachelor is lucky to have you, and he knows it.

Grace: *(sniffling.)* I just don't understand.

Candies: *(patting her hand.)* We'll figure it out. Let's just go home for now, okay? You can rest and we'll see what happens in the morning.

Grace: *(nodding.)* Okay. Thank you for being here, Candies.

Candies: *(smiling.)* Of course, Grace. That's what friends are for.

Grace: I am so grateful for your support, my friend. I do not know what I would have done without you.

Grace :(*Frustration and disappointment still lingered in her heart.)*

I cannot help but wonder what has gone wrong, and why have it has left me waiting for so long.

Candies: I am here for you now. Wait for him to touch you tomorrow or so.

Grace: Thank you, my friend.

(As they left the restaurant and stepped out into the cool autumn night, the stratocumulus clouds are in tears. Grace tries to shake off her disappointment and focuses on the moment. But deep down, she knew that the memory of this night would stay with her for a long time.)

Exeunt

7.5.2 Scene Two

(At night, on the road, two vehicles; one a Ford Ranger and One a Mercedes Benz. The Ford Ranger is coming from the north and Mercedes the Benz from the south; the sky is filled up with stratocumulus clouds, it is cold and raining)

Bachelor :*(Inside a Ford Ranger, Bachelor in high emotion and anticipation.)*

Bachelor: I hope I find him. I have always felt such deep a connection with you, deep in my thoughts and heart I have never hated you.

Casanova :*(Inside a Mercedes Benz, Casanova in high emotion and anticipation.)*

Casanova: Whatever separated us, it shall be put in the past. I cannot lose you again. I have always felt such entanglement with you, which I couldn't understand.

(Inside a Ford Ranger, Bachelor in high emotion and anticipation.)

Bachelor: Losing you again shall cripple my heart more than it already has. I so desire to see you to embrace you-and give you a kiss.

(Inside a Mercedes Benz, Casanova in high emotion and anticipation.)

Casanova: I hope I find you. You're close by, my instincts are telling me.

(Exhilarated): What an eagerness I have; exhilarated am I to see you! In all that we've been through, it wasn't hatred, but selfishness and pride had been ingrained in my heart; I never despised you. SBWL for us to come across each other. The zealousness I have, to set

267

my eyes on you; thereby we embrace and give each other a platonic kiss, that we never had a chance before.

(As they drive on the road, by the ocean; waves raging, the sky gloomy with stratocumulus clouds, rain pouring, cooling and cold breeze inserts inside the skin and nostrils, they come across each other; thereafter each stops his vehicle on pavement by the coast; they stand still, stare and gaze deeply at each other's blazing blue eyes; their eyes filled with tears and heart with deep sorrow, they are shivering and freezing; as they are both wearing clothes for mild cool autumn weather.)

Bachelor :*(Mixed emotions.)* Casanova! Casanova! At last, I have found you.

Casanova: *(Mixed emotions.)* Bachelor! Bachelor! You are here; I have found you.

(They run to each other, and make a steadfast magnetic embracement, showing such stronghold platonic love, kiss each other's lips and chicks; stand upright embracing, with each one's head on each other's shoulders as the rain pours from the sky.)

Casanova: I am so sorry for whatever misdemeanour I have enticed on you. Please find it in your heart to pardon me. All this time, I have been such a fool; living a life, full of frivolity, and futility. Truth be said: all my actions had been embedded in self-centredness.

(Entangled in such a magnetic embracement, as the rain pours from the heavens, with gloomy atmosphere, the waters from the sea releasing roaring sounds, waves raging across the rocky shore.)

Bachelor: I couldn't be more appeased, pardon me for all the mean words and insults I have called you- sabotaging your relationships to settle scores. Moreover-know that, as of this moment; I am now at ease and complete. My heart sought for you, my mind wanted you-as for my spirit and soul, they needed you. It wasn't eroticism but platonic entanglement with you I sought.

(Tightened in each other's bodies and wet, but feeling warmth in their embracement.)

Casanova: *(Crying.)* So have I... (*weeps.*) All this time, chasing after women, sought pleasures, and chased for love- was all chasing after wind; that was not what my heart and soul wanted: All I wanted was you. All this time, hurting so many people; in the name of love -not aware the only love I needed was yours. I love you with steadfast anchoring love. I could be nowhere else than with you.

(Tightened in each other's bodies and wet, but feeling warmth in their embracement.)

Bachelor: I sought love in wrong places, frustrated and shuttering; but now, my heart is deepened in amusement and myrrh-with you in my arms. I love you with an incomparable love that cannot be described neither measured. The love I have for you is stronghold and unwavering. The blooms shall sooth in spring, wither in autumn; die in winter, glow in summer I am here with you.

(They look up the heavens filled with clouds and pouring rain, with tears of joy on their face. They laugh and cry, weep and giggle in each other's arms, completely wet.)

Casanova: As Autumn comes and tarnishes the vegetation, dropping lush leaves on the ground, thereafter winter furthers with withering; leaving trees naked on a barren landscape. Spring shall come with a regrowth of grassland and woodland-replenishing the meadow with sprouting roses, and then summer shall come, full of life-birds singing across the lively soothing trees. I'll be with you.

Bachelor: That's deep, I'm over the moon. As we are standing by the ocean whereby beyond these dark skies covered by stratocumulus clouds- lies Milky Way galaxy, a cosmic tapestry of stars and mysteries. Just as its countless constellations illuminate the night sky, my love for you illuminates my very being. With each breath I take, I am reminded of the infinite beauty that resides within us, entwined and inseparable.

(The rain pours hard, lightning and thunder strike, he pauses for a moment.)

Casanova: And if the Milky Way is but a glimpse of the universe's vastness, then the 110 million light year Virgo Super cluster to the 520 million expanse of the Laniakea Super cluster are testaments to the expansiveness of our love.

(They look straight at each other's glowing blue eyes, kiss each other's chicks and hold tightly to one another.)

Bachelor: As for that, across these unimaginable distances, our connection transcends time and space, binding us together in a cosmic dance. For in the grand tapestry of the 93 billion light-year universe, our love is a radiant star, shining bright amidst the darkness. Its warmth guides me through the uncertainties of life, reminding me of the infinite possibilities that love brings.

Casanova: I couldn't be more elated. *(They pause for moments; there is silence as rain pours; lightning striking across the gloomy heavens, followed by thunder.)* Let's go home, it's raining cats and dogs now, accompanied by lightning and thunderstorms across the stratosphere, filled with darkened clouds.

Bachelor: What are we going to do?

Casanova: I have a rope we can use to pull the other car, will drive one vehicle-yours; since it has more horse power.

Bachelor: Excellent idea, it is raining and I am so wet; we are so wet.

Casanova: Yes, let's go tie them so we can go. *(They refrain from embracement, Casanova goes and opens the boot of the vehicle, and takes out the rope; Bachelor crosses his Ford Ranger to the left side of the road and faces it northwards, in front of the Mercedes Benz. They connect the two vehicles, embrace, then get inside Ford Ranger, take off their clothes; put them in a plastic, thereby turn on the heater and drive way northwards.)*

Exeunt

7.5.3 Scene Three

(At 11:30 p.m. Green Point, Cape Town; an apartment building with a grand postmodern architecture; the lobby is spacious and lit, with polished marble floors and a glass chandelier hanged from the ceiling.

The catch takes you, in a 21st century style lift to the fifth floor where Valentine and Sharon's apartment is.

I nside, you're welcomed by a cosy and warm living space. The living room has a plush sofa set, with comfortable cushions and throws, and a glass coffee table in the centre. The walls are painted in a muted grey tone, contrasting nicely with the dark wood flooring. The curtains are drawn, shutting out the view of the rain pouring outside.

The kitchen is modern and functional, with a sleek black countertop and stainless-steel appliances. The cabinets are white, with a glossy finish that reflects the soft glow of the lights.)

Valentine: I can't believe it. After all these years, I have finally found him.

Sharon: I know. It's amazing. But I can't believe Helen kept this from you and your family for all this time.

Valentine: I had to confront her. I couldn't just let her get away with it. The DNA result came out 99.99% positive, and have already got plausible information from Vredehoek Orphanage Centre that is overwhelming, even without the DNA test result that confirms Casanova is our brother.

Sharon: And what did she say?

Valentine: She admitted everything. She said that she found out about Casanova being our brother after she adopted him in 1993. But she didn't want to tell us because she was afraid of how we would react. What shocked and puzzled me the most was the illegality of this adoption with the help of Delilah, who worked there at the dawn of the 1990s.

Sharon: I can't believe she denied that in your face. And what about Casanova? Did he believe you?

Valentine: He stormed in demanding answers, but we told him everything. He's gone to look for Bachelor himself. I said I can take him, he said, no; he shall look for him himself. He was infuriated at us for hiding to Bachelor that he had a twin. He called us both liars. I don't know what am I going to do, how am I going to face Bachelor.

Sharon: I just hope he finds him soon. They've been separated for far too long, and it is plausible why he wants to look for him himself; they have known each other for years, and even hating each other. Their twin-hood bondage needs to be built by themselves, without you or anyone else imposing.

Valentine: (*emotional.*) It even scared me to go home. That is why I picked you up and come here.

Sharon: I shall always be there for you, hey.

Valentine: Thank you very much. (In fear). But then, something stroked me.

Sharon: (*curious.*) What?

Valentine: Helen mentioned she suspects Delilah might be the main orchestrator in murdering our parents. I just cannot stop thinking about it.

Sharon: (*Shocked.*) What!

Valentine: (*Sighs.*) Yes, and on top of it; when I went to see that prisoner, he mentioned something about another hand behind that horrendous act.

Sharon: You need to go see him again.

Valentine: I don't think he would. He has been there for almost 18 years now, and he does not care.

Sharon: Reason with him, maybe for a reduced sentence.

Valentine: *(frighten.)* And do that why? He has already caused so much pain and suffering in my family.

Sharon: *(Sighs.)* Look, do you want to know the actual orchestrator of your parent's murder?

Valentine: Yes.

Sharon: Then go speak to him. I am not saying he may get it, since he has not shown remorse: but whether he is or not, justice must be served.

Exeunt

7.5.4 Scene Four

(In the early morning, the sky is partially cloudy, with stratus clouds creating a misty and atmospheric effect. Fish Hoek, A Suburban Family home. Enter Mrs Andrews and Mr Andrews.)

Mr Andrews: *(looking out the window.)* It's a bit gloomy morning, today. The stratus clouds are partially covering the sky.

Mrs Andrews: *(preparing breakfast.)* Yes, it's almost overcast. But I don't mind, it's perfect weather for a warm English breakfast.

Mr Andrews: *(sighing.)* Portia, I just wanted to say that I am deeply sorry for what I did. I know I have hurt you and I regret it every day.

Mrs Andrews: *(turning around.)* I appreciate your apology, but it doesn't change what happened. I trusted you, John. How could you do this to us?

Mr Andrews: *(looking down.)* I don't know what came over me. I was weak and foolish. But I promise you, it will never happen again.

Mrs Andrews: *(sighing.)* John, I'm not perfect either. I know I neglected our relationship and I was distant. Maybe if I had been there for you, this wouldn't have happened.

Mr Andrews: *(smiling.)* Don't blame yourself, Portia. It was my mistake, not yours. And I promise to make it up to you and be a better husband.

Charles: *(walking in.)* Good morning, mom and dad.

Mrs Andrews: *(smiling.)* Good morning, sweetie. How was your shower?

Charles: *(yawning.)* It was great. What's for breakfast?

Mrs Andrews: *(placing the plates on the table.)* Scrambled eggs, Russian, bacon, and toast.

Charles: *(excitedly.)* Yum! It smells delicious.

Mr Andrews: *(smiling.)* Yes, your mom is the best cook in the world.

Mrs Andrews: *(giggling.)* Flattery will get you nowhere, John.

Charles: *(smiling.)* I'm just glad you guys have made up. It's not good for the family to be fighting.

Mr Andrews: *(nodding.)* You're right, son. We should always put family first.

Mrs Andrews: *(smiling.)* Absolutely. Now let's enjoy this lovely breakfast and the beautiful season of late autumn.

Exeunt

7.5.5 Scene Five

(Green Point, Cape Town, A Mansion; in the mid-morning, the sky scattered with status clouds; the sun trying to break through them, creating a calming scene with a cooling breeze from the Atlantic Ocean. In the bedroom overlooking the Atlantic Ocean, enter Bachelor and Casanova in bed cuddled and full agitation.)

Casanova: I cannot believe after all these years on each other's throat, we have been related. I still cannot believe to be sleeping with you here.

Bachelor: Me too, twin. I have never felt such affection. I knew I missed something in life but did not know it was you.

Casanova: Me too twin, I am overwhelmed with agitation. It really rained last night, and we couldn't refrain from each other.

Bachelor: True indeed. It was destined by God. I think had Valentine came along with you, none of this would have happened.

Casanova: It wouldn't have had. I was infuriated and inflamed-left Helen and him in tears, and went out to search for you. My heart overwhelmed with vexation, to have found you and know my true identity. I have never seen them-our parents! I am sure you feel the same as well, but I am exhilarated to be with you.

Bachelor: Indeed. If it wasn't the photos I've shown you, I wouldn't have a picture of them. But, at least we have each other.

Casanova: *(sighs.)* For the better. *(They pause for a moment, holding each other.)*

Casanova: *(Curious.)* You were so well-dressed last night. Did you come to see me so dressed nicely?

Bachelor: (Laughing.) Not at all. I actually had a date last evening. I was disturbed by the shocking news, seeing those DNA result laying there on the table.

Casanova: (Smiling.) A date?

Bachelor: Yes, a date. It's a girl I met at Green Point Soccer stadium.

Casanova: I didn't know you were into soccer, even saw you on TV. That was quite impressive. Congratulations.

Bachelor: Thanks.

Casanova: Tell me about her. Who is she?

(Pauses for moment, and looks at Casanova.)

Casanova: Don't worry, I won't do that. You had even changed me, even before we discovered we are related. (pauses). Trust me, bro.

Bachelor: (Smiling.) If you do, I will kill you.

Casanova: (Smiling.) Yes...(*curiosity.*)

Bachelor: Her name is Grace. She is so beautiful with Nordic features like Precious.

Casanova: I guess we have the same taste and presence. Remember, you also wanted Ntombi once.

Bachelor: (Giggling.) And you bastard, you took her. *(Hitting him with a pillow.)*

Casanova: I am sorry, hey. You should call her. I am sure it must have inflicted her, having stood her up all night.

Bachelor: I will. (Taking a cell phone from the bedside.) It's completely flat.

Casanova: Mine too.

Bachelor: So, what's next? What are you going to do with Precious? If you truly love her, don't give up on her. I now see- that you are meant to be together.

Casanova: I will reach out to her; I cannot give up. I love her so much.

Bachelor: And if she does not want you back?

Casanova: I am going to stay single, take time to process all of this and heal, have a time to bond with you and Valentine and focus on what I want to do next year.

Bachelor: Wow. That is so mature of you; you are truly reborn.

Casanova: Yes, I am. So, what are you going to do next year?

Bachelor: I am planning to for university, don't which on yet.

Casanova: Same as I. I took a gap year, to see what I truly want and not rush into academia, then regret later, having completed a degree I do not want and will not help me in a digitally revolutionising economy.

Bachelor: Wow, we have so much in common, hey?

Casanova: I am so hungry, let's go make some breakfast, it's already 09:30 a.m. I just feel at home. I haven't even finished a day here.

Bachelor: You are at home. Feel free, navigate and take whatever that you want. No need to ask me. Let's take a shower then we go make it. (*They go take a shower.*)

(*In a few minutes, they have come out of the bathroom dressed in morning gowns: in the kitchen, Bachelor and Casanova are preparing breakfast, chatting and laughing together.*)

Casanova: I still can't believe we found each other after all these years. I am so exceedingly elated by our fondness

Bachelor: I know, right? It's like something out of a movie.

Casanova: And to think we were both living in Cape Town this whole time, went to the same high school and in the same class!

Bachelor: Yeah, it's crazy. But I'm just glad we're together now.

(*Valentine enters the kitchen unexpectedly.*)

Valentine: (*feeling sad.*) Good morning, boys. I hope I'm not interrupting anything.

Casanova: (*surprised.*) Valentine! I didn't expect to see you here.

Bachelor: (*Frowns.*) I can't believe you lied to me all this time, if only you knew how much quarrelsome I have had with Canova.

Valentine: *(Valentine's heart weighed heavy as he looks at Bachelor.)*

Valentine: *(Voice slightly shaking.)* I'm sorry, Bachelor, I should have told you about Casanova a long time ago. I should have told you that you had a twin brother out there somewhere.

Bachelor :*(looks up at him with understanding in his eyes.)*

Bachelor: It's okay, Valentine. I'm just glad we're all together now. We can't change the past, but we can make things right from now on.

Valentine :(nodding with tears welling up in his eyes.) Thank you very much. I can't believe you have forgiven me so easily after all the pain I have caused by hiding the truth for so long, and you, Casanova; I am sorry for not doing much to look for you all these years.

Bachelor and Casanova: (Afflicted.) It's okay, we forgive you. That is what family is for.

Valentine: *(Placing hands on both Bachelor's and Casanova's shoulders.)* I promise to make it up to you I'll do whatever it takes to make things right between us.

Bachelor: I'm not mad at you, Valentine. I understand why you didn't tell me. And I'm just happy to have found Casanova.

Casanova: Me too. We ran into each other on the road between Green Point and Hout Bay last night when it was raining.

Valentine: Wow, what a miracle! What are the chances? And now you're here together, making breakfast. You made an excellent, godly decision to go and look for each other on your own.

Bachelor: Yeah, we're more united than ever. I told Casanova about how our parents died when we were just a few months old.

Casanova: It was tough to hear, but I'm glad we both know the truth and are united now.

Valentine: I'm glad you two have found each other. As Richard Green's children, we should all be united.

(The three of them share a group hug.)

Casanova: This is the best English breakfast I've ever had.

Bachelor: It's because we made it together. Like true brothers.

Valentine: I couldn't be happier to see you two together. Now let's eat and celebrate our newfound family bond. It's Sunday. Do you want us to go to Church, maybe? Praise and thank God.

Bachelor and Casanova: Yes, we'd be enthralled.

Exeunt

7.5.6 Scene Six
(Hout Bay Helen's Hotel, Helen's office)

HELEN: *(Frustrated.)* Oh, what a mess I have found myself in. How could I have known that the adoption of Casanova was not legitimate?

Helen: *(Condescending.)* I did what I thought was best for him, but now I fear the consequences of my actions. And now, with Bachelor and Casanova discovering that they are twins, the truth may come out, and everything is going to unravel.

Helen: *(Sighs.)* I have been so relieved since Delilah informed me, she would no longer implicate me in the deaths of Richard and Bridget Green.

(She leans back in her chair, looks out at the window, with wind blowing from the seas with status clouds across the sky.)

Helen: *(Exhales deeply.)* But now, with her demands to sabotage Valentine's relationship with Sharon, I fear she will pull me back into the web of lies and deceit once again.

(She pauses for a moment, senses cooling breeze from the cold bunguela current.)

Helen: *(buoyant.)* But it seems it is too late for that. I am sanguine for that Valentine has already found out the truth about his brothers, and nothing can change that now. Delilah's anger and frustration only add to my distress, but I cannot let her drag me down with her.

(Helen is having some mixed emotions and distressed.)

Helen: *(Pessimistic.)* This situation just keeps getting worse and worse. How could I have been so foolish to adopt Casanova illegally? The truth is bound to come out now that Bachelor and Casanova have discovered they are twins, and it even already has, since Valentine mentioned it yesterday. What do I do? Why did I lie to Casanova all this time? I even said his parents were drug addicts.

(She brushes her head and face, puts her arms on her lap and then on the table.)

Helen: *(Expectant.)* But at least I don't have to worry about Delilah anymore. I am relieved that she won't be blackmailing me about the Greens' deaths.

(She stands up, goes to the window, looking at the partially clouded sky with dancing stratus clouds and waves raging on the beach.)

Helen: *(inhales the cool wind and exhales.)* But why does she have to be so difficult? She is demanding that we sabotage Valentine's relationship with Sharon. Doesn't she realize that it's too late for that? Valentine already knows the truth about his brothers. I can't believe she is threatening to have me arrested for adopting Casanova illegally. This is a nightmare.

(In a moment, Delilah budges in unexpected, Helen frightens and calms down.)

Delilah: Good day Helen. I hope you have thoroughly thought about our plan.

Helen: What are you talking about? It's too late for that. Valentine already knows the truth about his brothers.

Delilah: What do you mean he knows the truth? How could he find out?

Helen: He did a DNA test. He knows that Bachelor and Casanova are his brothers.

Delilah: This is a disaster. We have to do something.

Helen: There's nothing we can do. The truth is out. We just have to deal with the consequences.

Delilah: Consequences? You mean like the fact that you adopted Casanova illegally?

Helen: Don't even think about it. I won't let you implicate me in this any further.

Delilah: You don't have a choice. I can have you arrested for what you've done.

(In a moment, the police storm in; with Sylvia and Pretty behind them.)

1st Policeman: Good day

Helen and Delilah: Good Day *(Shivering.)*

2nd Policeman: You are both under arrest.

Delilah: For what?

1st Policeman: Delilah, you are under arrest for the orchestrated murder of Richard and Bridget Green on 15 June 1992, and for kidnaping an infant. You may remain silent. We can use anything you say against you in court. *(The policewoman tie her with handcuffs.)*

2nd Policeman: Helen, you are under arrest for illegally adopting a toddler back in 1993, with the help of Delilah, and kept about it quiet to this day. *(The policewoman ties her with handcuffs.)*

(Sylvia and Pretty are shocked, as the police are taking them to custody)

Helen: *(Resisting.)* No, no, I did not know, until later. I did nothing wrong.

Policewoman: You prove that in the Cape Town High Court. Ayiye madam. Asizanga kuzodlala apha!

Delilah: Do you know who I am? This is outrageous!

Policewoman: Mama! Hamba! Sigebengga ndini! You are both entitled to get a lawyer. If you do not have means, the state will provide for you.

Helen: Sylvia, do not just stand there, call my lawyer.

Sylvia: Okay ma'am

(The police apprehend Helen and Delilah, take them inside a van outside, all people in the reception bar and Kiosk stare with shutter and shock)

Pretty: My goodness, you were right when you said you may know nothing about this madam.

Sylvia: Shut up Pretty now, is not the time to gossip.

Exeunt

7.5.7 Scene Seven

(In a week. Fish Hoek, at noon. A restaurant by the beach; people are busy with a variety of activities such volleyball, basking, playing kite, children making sand castle: enter Precious)

Precious: *(sighs.)* If this guy does not pitch I am done with him, he summoned mere he and now he has not come; it has been 30 minutes. How can I be such a fool yet again? Why did even agree to meet him?

(He sees Casanova coming out of his car; towards the door of the restaurant.) Here he is. I hope he comes and talks some sense. What he did to me-lying, cheating and deception is uncalled for; uncouth, cruel and self-serving. It couldn't be more hurtfully, unto me or any other women who's been fooled by his treacherousness.

(Casanova comes towards the table and sits in front of Precious.)

Casanova: *(sighs.)* Good day, sorry for keeping you waiting.

Precious: *(irritated.)* What do you want Casanova?

Casanova: To pardon me for all the pain I have caused you; to apologise to you for all the women I have hurt. I shouldn't have done that.

Precious: *(ponders.)* Is this your way to get through me? Be remorseful to them.

Casanova: No, not at all. I feel reborn. I want to make amends, and do whatever it takes to make things right.

Precious: And you've decided to come now? You do not look like someone who is truly genuine. Where have you been all this time?

(Waitress comes.)

Waitress: Hi, what can I get you?

Casanova: Just two hakes, with some medium french-fries and chopped lemons.

Waitress: Sure, coming right up.

Casanova: Also bring in some hot lemonade. I want some Vitamin C; I feel like I am going to have some cold and fever.

Waitress: Cool. I'll be back just now.

Exit

Casanova: *(Sighs and looks at Precious).* A lot has happened, Precious, but I couldn't be happier, though it has aggrieved and crippled my heart.

Precious: *(rolling eyes.)* Here we go again, you and excuses. *(Sips a cup of coffee.)*

Casanova: *(emotional.)* Bachelor is my twin brother.

Precious: *(the sip gets into the trachea and spits it.)*

Precious: (Shocked.) What!

Casanova: *(sighs.)* Yes. It's a long story.

Precious: But how? Is this some kind of joke?

(The waitress comes back and brings the order.)

Casanova: Thanks. *(Waitress leaves.)* No, it is not. Somewhere last week or so... that is when we discovered we are twin brothers. Valentine-his brother, is my elder brother as well.

Precious: *(Curious.)* I am just perplexed. How did all this happen? You guys have been into each other's throats as long as I can remember, and now you are twins? I am just bewildered by this.

Casanova: Back in 1992 on 21March, he and I were born. Valentine was 15 years. In winter that same year, our parents got killed. By luck, we got spared. Valentine was with the infant Bachelor inside in the kitchen and I was outside. I got kidnaped and dropped at Vredehoek Orphanage Centre and they named me Michael. At home, they named me Matthew. A year later, was adopted by my adoptive mother, Helen; and it was not legit. She collaborated with a woman named Delilah. Same Delilah, who orchestrated the murder of my parents.

Precious: (*Takes a deep breath.*) Shame... but then, how did you all find out?

Casanova: You all always say, Bachelor and I resemble each other. (Leans back on his chair.)

Precious: (curious.) Yea?

Casanova: (*Sighs.*) Apparently, Bachelor was having dinner with Valentine, Sharon, Charles and Ntombi, and this topic came up. And also, before that; I was at the beach with Bachelor, arguing and this stranger came and told us this resemblance appearance between us. So Valentine, eager to know the truth. He dug up, went to prison to find information from the culprit who killed our parents, he directed him to the orphanage centre. All that confirmed I am his twin.

Precious: (*Leans back on the chair.*) Wow! I do not even know what to say. And then what happened?

Casanova: Here is an interesting part. I was with Bachelor in some restaurant in Green Point; we spoke a lot. He challenged my behaviour, and I saw he was right. I felt some connection with him. In fact, I began to be calm with him from the moment we shook hands at the beach. What happened is: Sharon came and sat with us, she also noted this resemblance; what she did, she took the utensils I was using to eat and drink, and plucked up some hair from me, without my awareness and Bachelor. She gave that to Valentine and they did some DNA test, which confirmed that we are indeed twin brothers.

Precious: (*Amused.*) It makes sense now. All the puzzles show clearly that you are indeed related. You have the same style of dress code; you resemble each other; your chicks, your eyes, stature, hair and jaw; you even like the same women.

(*Leans forward on the table, sips a cup of coffee.*)

Precious: I know the story of Ntombi. So how did you and Bachelor handle this? How was your reaction? How did both of you find out?

Casanova: At dusk, Bachelor was planning on going on a date, when he stumbled upon the DNA results laying on the table.

Precious :(*surprised.*) Bachelor on a date?

Casanova: Yes. I'll tell you more in time. He was shuttered, shivering, and shocked. He did not go to the date; he went straight looking for me.

(He takes a bite and swallows.)

Casanova: On the other side, Valentine came and confronted my mother about this. I overheard them talking.

Casanova*: (emotional.)* I stormed in, demanded some answers. They both admitted. I was dismayed and disconcert; confused and frustrated. I left immediately to look for him.

Precious: (Astounded.) An' did you find him?

Casanova :(face falls, and cries.) We came across each other in a gloomy overcast, raining night with altocumulus. When we said; I have found you calling each other's name. We ran to each other and embraced, kissed each other, expressed how we love each other.

Precious: (*Emotional.*) That must have been afflicting, yet comforting and amazing. (*Giving him a tissue.*)

Casanova: (Tears weeping, and wipes them.) I have never felt like that before. I have been with many girls, but the hugs and kisses we had, brought such an alluring affection, I felt loved for the first time. While the rain was pouring, we could not let go of each other. We cried, we laughed; we were sorrowful and smiling. I felt deep loneliness, and all ills in my heart erased. We felt such stronghold compassion, purity, benediction, innocence and intense platonic love.

Precious: *(Takes a deep breath.)* It all makes sense now. You and he are the same. Your souls sought connection and love in wrong places. You both couldn't find what your spirits sought.

Casanova: Exactly. I have lived such a frivolous lifestyle, with deceit and misdemeanours; hurting people who are innocent, while what I needed was right in front of me, furthermore; in quarrelsome with it.

Precious: I am so afflicted by this, sorry for undergoing such infliction. I can only imagine what you and Bachelor have gone through. Moreover, I am glad now, that you have fixed your issues and found one another.

Casanova: Yes, I am so agitated, I couldn't be more elated than I am currently.

Precious: So have the two been apprehended?

Casanova: Yes. Thank God that the prisoner revealed the truth when he was summoned on a parole board. I don't know if they shall reduce his sentence. It could even go to the Supreme Court in Bloemfontein. But as for Delilah, she is going to be there for a long time. She had even started a conspiracy to sabotage Valentine's marriage, but the truth coming out ruined that.

Precious: And your mother?

Casanova: Only time shall tell, she might get a suspended sentence or some few years. But I have forgiven her. We all have forgiven hair. She even pleaded that she gave us her shares at Helen's Hotel.

Precious: *(reaching out her hand to Casanova.)* Let us hope for the best now, for you and Bachelor.

Casanova: I am assuring all the best is coming. Thank you very much. I love you Precious, please forgive for all the ills I have caused you.

Precious: Let us put this all behind us, and look for the better future. *(They embrace over the table.)*

Exeunt

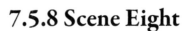

7.5.8 Scene Eight

(Kirstenbosch National Botanical Garden: a warm glow of light spills into the stage, illuminating a breath-taking scene. It is in the mid-afternoon the sun is casting long shadows across the landscape; the sky is a warm orange hue, with the sun halfway to setting, signalling the approach of evening; enter Bachelor and Grace walking.)

Grace: I am glad you have explained to me. The way you deserting me that day mortified me.

Bachelor: I am so sorry, I couldn't think of anything else but him. I felt so betrayed that all my life has been a lie.

Grace: It is even worse that you have been quarrelling with your twin.

Bachelor: True indeed. But there's still much to enjoy and fulfilment ahead. I am still young, haven't explored the ruminations of life.

(He looks around the trees, and the sky.)

Bachelor: Most of my life, I have been comparing myself with others, being pressured to be like most dudes. I couldn't understand my true desire. In all of that, it was right in front of me: in the meantime, immersed in intra-conflict with myself and inter-conflict with him. I have been blindfolded and could not see the signs.

Grace: It must have been distressful. *(Grabbing and squeezing hand.)* But then you have found what makes you complete.

Bachelor: (takes a deep breath and exhales, looking over the birds singing, flying across the trees and sky.)

Bachelor: *(intense.)* True indeed. On that day, with rain pouring over our bodies. I felt like I was being lifted by the waves of the sea across the starry heavens. I felt contempt and complete.

(Feeling emotional and weeping tears.)

Bachelor: *(sorrowful voice.)* I felt sorrow; I felt myrrh. Our souls were so intertwined that all pain, all grief, all lamentation, all disappointment, all betrayal, all frustration and distressfulness were erased. It was cold, but we felt warmth and comfort.

(Takes a deep breath and feels at ease.)

Bachelor: I can never explain the innocence and sweetness that we felt in each other's arms. I felt steadfast love I had never felt. The kisses and embracement we had, were so cheerful and uplifting. *(He pauses for a moment in thought.)* I love Valentine, my brother... but Casanova... I feel like I love him much more.

Grace: Wow. You truly love each other. I cannot wait to meet him. *(They stop and gaze upon each other.)*

Bachelor: You will, *(They embrace.)* and maybe we could go on a double date with him and Precious. He just texted me a few minutes ago that he has fixed things with her.

Grace: That would be awesome. *(Smiling.)*

(The orange sun raises shine across the cloudy western sky.)

Bachelor: I feel so amazed, so complete when I am with you, with your beautiful eyes as doves in the pool of crystal waters in winter.

Grace: *(Smiling.)* I couldn't be happier and anywhere else than here. (They embrace.)

Bachelor: I love you. (They kiss).

Grace: I love you too. *(They kiss).*

Exeunt

7.5.9 Scene Nine

(It's a late autumn, in the afternoon in Fish Hoek, Cape Town, and the clear sky and gentle waves make for a peaceful scene on the beach. Rose, Cynthia, Amanda, and Ntombi stand on the boardwalk, looking out at the beautiful coastline.", they are wearing Bafana Bafana Jersey)

Amanda: Yeah, it's been too long for me too.

Ntombi: *(looking at the shore.)* The coast is so beautiful here, especially in the late afternoon with clear skies like this.

Cynthia: *(joining the group.)* Hey, guys. How's it going?

Rose: Hey, Cynthia. We were just admiring the view.

(There is silence. They gaze upon the waves and some guys surfing.)

Amanda: (breaks the silence.) Can you believe Casanova cheated on all of us? I can't believe I fell for his lies.

Rose: *(nods in agreement.)* Yeah, I thought he was the one for me, but I guess we all got played. I am so sorry for fighting you, Amanda, over him.

Ntombi: *(in a moment after silence.)* I always knew he was no good. I cannot believe he fooled all of us. It is even worse for you, Rose; you went for him knowing well what he was doing.

Rose: I thought I would change him.

(Cynthia, who had been listening to their conversation, while busy on her Black Berry Curve 8520, scanning through emails, and sending hers; chimes in.)

Cynthia: Well, I have some news about Casanova. He recently found out that Bachelor is his twin.

(The three ex-girlfriends look at each other in.)

Amanda: *(Contemplating.)* Bachelor? That guy Casanova always rivals with?

Cynthia :(nods.) Yes, that's the one. He is a friend of my boyfriend Charles. It turns out they didn't even know they were brothers until Valentine, their older brother, found out.

Ntombi :(*looks sceptical.*) It is hard to believe-Casanova and Bachelor always seemed to hate each other.

Cynthia: (*shrugs.*) Well, that's what Precious told me. She's still dating Casanova-you know?

(*The three ex-girlfriends exchange a knowing look.*)

Rose: (sighs.) Well, I'm just glad we're all done with him. Let's go grab some soft serve and forget about that jerk.

Amanda: let's all first take a selfie. (She *takes out, her Black Berry Torch 9800, then they all get one another, and take* a *selfie*).

Cynthia: Wow, you have Black Berry Torch? It has such mesmerising pictures.

Amanda: Casanova have me as a gift.

Rose: (*Infuriated.*) That bastard, the only thing I got from him are roses, the vuvuzela and this bangle.

Amanda: Don't cry now dear, I'm even thinking of selling this phone, if not just throw away, I don't want anything that that shall remind me of him.

Cynthia: How are we going to get this image then?

Amanda: We have blue tooth right...

Ntombi: Let's do it now. If you have anything with you now, got from Casanova, let's all throw them away.

Amanda: (Acclimated.) What! Do you understand what you are asking me to do?

Ntombi: Materialism is not everything, we all want to put him behind for heart breaking us , what's important is for our minds to be at peace.

Amanda: I see. (*In agreement*). Let me send these pictures. Cynthia, I'll send them to you. (They *connect with* a *blue tooth, and sends the images.*)

Ntombi: Now it's time. I'm throwing away this 9 CT golden watch.

Rose: I'm throwing away this bangle.

Amanda: *(pauses, with doubts for a moment.)* Are you guys serious?

Cynthia: Look, you've all been fractured mentally, emotionally, physically and spiritually – you're all fragmented. I am not saying you should do this, because Casanova chose my sister, which I had a hand in getting her involved with him. But he's not worth it, I feel your affliction. Whether Casanova has come to right senses, and lives a life full of integrity and honour, he'll not come back to you. This cell phone, is going to give you a heart beat. Start afresh, take a break from boys and dating, and focus on building yourself. You can play bitcoin to make some money quick and buy a new black berry torch .

Amanda: Yes – I guess you are right. (*Amanda throws the cell phone into the sea, some guys near by are* **shocked**.)

1st Guy: What! Did you just throw away a Black Berry Torch 8900?

2nd Guy: You're crazy! Do you know how expensive that is.

Rose: Mind your business, get way from here . (*The guys go.*)

Cynthia: That was brave of you Amanda. (*She embraces her.*)

Ntombi: Let me do the same. (*She throws* away *the watch*)

Rose: I might as well. (*She throws away the bangle.*) What I've realised in this moment. It doesn't matter how valuable the gift is, all of them were given out of deceit and manipulation, furthermore; no one was genuinely loved. Let's embrace and move on.

Ntombi: Well said Rose. Sisterhood all the away. We can't let ourselves be played like this by men, and end up fighting each other.

Cynthia: Spot on guys, I'm very proud of you.

Amanda: Let's go get some fun guys.

(The four women walk off the boardwalk towards the beach, leaving their past with Casanova behind them.)

Exeunt

7.5.10 Scene Ten

(The cool autumn evening breeze gently swirled through the air in Hout Bay, as Casanova and Bachelor made their way to Helen's Hotel. The sky painted with hues of orange and pink, setting the perfect backdrop for the evening ahead. As they entered the hotel; in the reception area of Helen's Hotel. Sylvia and Pretty are at the reception desk. Casanova enters, with Bachelor following closely behind. He confidently approached the reception desk, with Bachelor following closely behind.)

Casanova: Good evening, ladies. It's good to see you both again.

Sylvia: *(smiling.)* Hi, Casanova. How can we assist you today?

Casanova: *(grinning.)* Actually, I have some news to share with you. This is my twin brother, Bachelor. We recently found out that we are twins.

(Sylvia and Pretty looked up, momentarily taken aback by the handsome pair in front of them.)

Sylvia: (surprised.) Really? That's amazing news. **Congratulations!**

Pretty: *(whispers to Sylvia.)* They're both so handsome! I yearn if we could have just a chance with them. I can't help how irresistible they are; how wonderful would it be if we could win their hearts.

Sylvia: *(hushed tone.)* Don't be silly, Pretty. We can't talk about that now. *(Sylvia quickly hushes her.)*

Casanova: (noticing their exchange.) We are currently selecting a manager for the hotel. We're here on business.

Sylvia: (smiling.) Of course. So, what brings you both here?

Casanova: (proudly.) We're actually the new share owners of this hotel, as from this evening.

Sylvia: *(impressed.)* Wow, that's great news! **Congratulations** to both of you.

Bachelor: (smiling.) Thank you. We're excited to take on this new venture.

Sylvia: (nodding approvingly.) I'm sure you'll do a fantastic job. So, who will manage the hotel?

Casanova*: (confidently.)* For now, my brother and I will manage it ourselves. We are fortunate to have been born in families that have taught us business and managerial skills from childhood in our homes, so we're more than capable of running the hotel. Nevertheless, we shall look for the new manager soon, maybe someone of your expertise Sylvia. I adore and aspire your professionalism, enthusiasm and business ethics, despite the history we have. Your dedication to make this hotel function is honourable and praiseworthy.

Sylvia: (*eyes widened in surprise.*) Oh thank you very much. I am fluttered. *(They embrace.)* That's great to hear.*(refraining from embracing.)* I wish you both the best of luck in this new endeavour.

(Casanova and Bachelor head towards their new office.)

Casanova: *(thinking out loud.)* We have a lot of work to do, but I'm confident that we can make this hotel a success.

Bachelor: *(nodding in agreement.)* Yeah, we should focus on improving the hotel's facilities and services.

Casanova: *(smiling.)* Exactly. We need to make this hotel the best in Hout Bay.

(Bachelor nods in agreement, and they plan their next moves.)

Exeunt

7.5.11 Scene Eleven

(In a week, the late autumn sun is dipping below the horizon, casting a warm golden light across the town square of Fish Hoek. Max had just finished his shift at the local bookstore and was taking a leisurely stroll through the square when he saw Leah walking towards him.
Leah enters stage left, spotting Max and approaching him with a soft expression. The late autumn sky scatters cumulus clouds across the heavens, and a gentle sea breeze blows through the square, rustling the leaves on the trees and the flowers in the nearby gardens. A few people pass by, walking their dogs or chatting with friends. We can hear the sound of cars in the distance.)

Leah: *(softly voice, her eyes filled with regret.)* Hey Max.
    (Max's expression darkened as he remembered the reason he was so displeased with her.)

Max: *(coldly.)* What do you want, Leah?

Leah: *(takes a deep breath.)* I wanted to apologize for what I did to Valentine and Sharon's relationship. I didn't know my mother had planned such a foolish and selfish way to get me in bed with Valentine so that Sharon could dump him.

Max: *(disbelieving.)* You didn't know? You could have just said no, Leah. You didn't have to go along with it.

Leah: *(tearfully.)* I know, Max. I was stupid and selfish. I let my personal vendetta against Sharon cloud my judgment, and I was so lovesick for Valentine that I didn't see what was really happening.

(Leah's eyes filled with tears, Max's heart sank as Leah continued to speak.)

Leah: You know, Max, *(wiping away her tears.)* I think I realized something just now. You've always been there for me, and I never

298

really appreciated it. I think I've been in love with the wrong person all along.

(*Max's heart skips a beat as he hears Leah's words, quickly composes himself.*)

Max: (darkly.) You know, Leah, I think I realized something just now. You've always been there for me, and I never really appreciated it. I think I've been in love with the wrong person all along.

Leah*: (hopeful.)* What do you mean, Max?

Max: (heartfelt.) I mean that I've loved you for years, but I've never had the courage to tell you. And now, after everything that's happened, I realize that you were caught up in your own drama and never saw me in that way.

Leah: *(shocked.)* I did not know, Max. I never thought...

Max: *(interrupting.)* It doesn't matter now, Leah. I'm sorry; I'm no longer interested in you, even if I have been or am still in love with you.

Max: (*irritated and shaking his head.*) *I* cannot be with you; for you and your mother are the same. She orchestrated Valentine's parents back in 1992 and kidnapped Valentine's younger brother's twin, Casanova.

(*Looks people passing by and cars hooting, with rustling leaves blown by the wind.*)

Max: You and your mother are both manipulative and selfish, and I want nothing to do with either of you.

Leah: (heartbroken.) Max, please...

Max: (firmly.) No, Leah. It's over between us. I'm sorry.

(*Max turns and walks away, leaving Leah standing there, devastated and full of regret. As he leaves, a few more people pass by, some carrying bags of groceries or pushing strollers. The smell of roses and other flowers fills the air, and a few leaves rustle across the ground, blown by the sea breeze.*)

Leah: (*her body trembles as* <u>he</u> *falls* <u>to</u> *her* <u>knees</u>, *tears streaming* down her face).

Leah: (Shivering) What have I done, whom do I have now? It has caught me up with my self-engrailment and drama, and even pushed Nicole away, my only friend.

(*She sobs uncontrollably, her chest heaving as she struggles to breathe. Her face contorts with pain and regret, her eyes red and swollen from crying.*)

Leah: (*heartache and feeling so down.*) I feel so completely alone and empty. It has stripped away everything I had ever known from me my own actions.

(*Her heart feels heavy, weighed down by the weight of her mistakes and her deep sense of loss.*)

Leah: Nicole has dissociated herself with me, after warning me long before this that I should let go of feelings I have for valentine.

(*Leah's heart crippled with heartache withered rustling leaves being blown across her face.*)

Leah: (*Takes a deep breath, feeling the cooling breeze from the cold Benguela current; gazing shivering cumulus clouds.*) I need to put myself together, for my career's sake. This is a lesson I shall never forget, only because of my foolishness and being self-centred, listening to my cruel, manipulative, deceitful, treacherous and murderous mother; who is now in jail and I am left alone.

(*The sound of cars fades away, birds flying across reddish, yellowish and orange leaves flying across being blown by the wind.*)

Exeunt

7.5.12 Scene Twelve

(The cosy restaurant is near the Parliament of the Republic of South Africa, providing a stunning view of the city lights. The street below is alive with the sound of cars passing by, and the soft breeze of the autumn night is gently rustling the trees nearby. Bachelor and Casanova arrive at the restaurant, both dressed in sleek suits that highlight their toned physiques. They make their way to the table where Grace and Precious are seated, looking stunning in their elegant dresses.)

Bachelor: Wow, you both look absolutely gorgeous tonight. The colours you're wearing are perfect for a date in the evening in autumn, with the sky scattered with cumulus clouds, and the glowing moon shining from above.

Precious: Thank you! We're so happy you guys suggested this place. The view is amazing.

(Outside you can see the old and modern architectural style building glowing with lights, dancing trees which have turned lush, with leaves withering some still turning yellow, orange and red dancing, some people riding cycles, cars stopping and passing by the red, orange and green robots lights.)

Casanova: True indeed, and I have to say, this is such a lovely night. Being here with you all, enjoying good food, drinks, and each other's company just feels so perfect. The soft glow of the candles, the warm atmosphere of the restaurant, and the pleasant chill of the autumn breeze outside all make this moment so magical.

Grace: It is so mesmerising, you can see the astounding calming Edwardian architectural style City Hall, the mesmerising Victorian architectural style Parliament; the city lights glowing, and streets full of life.

Casanova: Yeah, it's not too bad. But wait until you see the food. The waiter here knows his stuff.

(As the waiter arrives at the table, the couple's order dishes that complement the autumn season, with the waiter recommending a rich red wine to accompany the meal. The conversation flows easily, with Bachelor and Casanova reminiscing about their past.)

Casanova: So Grace, what do you do?

Grace: I am studying architect at the University of Cape Town.

Casanova: No wonder you adore the architecture of the city?

Grace: Yes, but I am keener on the colonial Dutch, Gothic, Romanticism, Georgian, and Victorian Architecture.

Casanova: That might sound politically incorrect. Some would get cringed hearing that, even in the Western world; there's forceful post-structuralism for both physical and intellectual architecture fuelled by the universities, media and governments.

Grace: Throw political correctness in the garbage and let's all use logic and reason. Postmodern architecture is so bad; it is so ugly. Go to Durban and Johannesburg, you shall see.

Bachelor: I can attest to that. Even Pietermaritzburg architecture is more calming and enthralling than that of Durban.

Precious: True indeed, I went to that side once; the architecture displeased me. Grahamstown might be a small city, but its architecture draws you upon, you gaze at buildings.

Grace: *(fascinated.)* I love that city; it has all the prerequisite for a city: variety and order, orientation and mystery, visible life; I have forgotten the others. Whether you come from Port Elizabeth or from East London; you are just captivated by the Georgian-Victorian and Gothic architecture.

(They take a bite and sip some drink.)

Bachelor: So Precious, what's your plan for next year?

Precious: I have been undecided whether wanted to go to the University of the Witwatersrand or the University of Stellenbosch, but now since I have this loving man; I can study computer science, or software engineering and robotics at either University of Cape Town or at Stellenbosch University.

Bachelor: That's great. Think thoroughly.

Casanova: *(Looking at her.)* Yes babe, if we truly love each other, we can make it; whether you are here or in Gauteng. You do not have to give up your dreams because of me.

Precious: Thank you, baby, but I still have eight months to think.

(There is a pause, then they all eat, and take a drink sip.)

Grace: So what about you guys?

Bachelor: We shall see what we can study to capacitate ourselves in running a hotel and a big company like Green and Sons Wine. I just hope this government under Jacob Zuma, can come up with sound policies, that can erase all red tape, but I don't trust him. He is going to mess up the ASGISA initiative, which has given us a growth of around 5% since it initiation in 2006, furthermore-that has already been hammered by the 2008 global financial crisis, causing our economy to shrink by 1.5%in 2009.

Grace: *(Amazed.)* Hmmm...I like your intellect. *(kisses him.)*

Precious: You are blessed, are you going to manage them on your own?

Casanova: Yes, my adoptive mother gave up her shares as her way to show remorse. It was actually 50% owned by our biological mother, and Helen owned the other 50%. After all that happened, which we know, she took the shares for herself. I am as pleased as Punch, that we are going to be running and managing it with the brother I love so dearly; we have split it to 50% between us.

Bachelor: I am elated and enthusiastic about undertaking this journey with you, Matthew.

Grace: Your other name is Matthew?

Casanova: (*Smiling.*) I have so many names: Matthew, Michael and Casanova.

Grace: Which one do you like?

Casanova: I don't know, but for now I'll just stick to Casanova, but I guess I can add the other two in my identity document, I've already applied for a New Green book to change my name from Smith to Green.

Bachelor: I like Casanova, so I can always remember how funny your life was.

(*They all laugh.*)

Precious: (*curious.*) So, do you guys have any skills and proficiencies to run a hotel?

Casanova: I can just say, we were fortunate enough to be born and raised in wealthy families, who had all the socioeconomic capital and network.

Bachelor: Indeed. By chance and luck, at home, they taught us we all the basic and fundamental business skills, which you cannot find in South Africa's basic education system. But then, we can study any business, economic and financially related degree next year at UCT. After all, that we have been through, we are now fonder of each other than ever.

Casanova: (*Recalling.*)Do you remember how we used to hate each other's guts back in the day?

Bachelor: Yeah, until that stranger at the beach made us shake hands and bury the hatchet.

Grace: What happened?

Bachelor: I realised Casanova was just hurting people because he was hurting himself. I had to talk some sense into him.

(*Inside you can see mesmerising furniture, waiters and waitresses serving guests with clean and smooth cutleries, with fine music playing.*)

Precious: I cannot explain how much I felt so betrayed, my heart with filled with havoc when I heard Casanova has cheated on me with three girls. Three girls Grace! (Laughing.)

Grace :(*laughing.)* He must have been going through some teenage swings.

Casanova: I am sorry, sweetheart.

Grace: And now look at him, all loved up; only because of you.

(Casanova looks over at Precious with a warm smile, taking her hand in his.)

Casanova: I have Bachelor to thank for that.

Grace: It's amazing how things work out, isn't it?

(As the night wears on, the couples continue to enjoy each other's company, savouring the delicious food and wine while laughing and chatting. The affection between them is palpable, with Bachelor and Grace sharing a sweet kiss and Casanova whispering sweet nothings into Precious' ear.)

Casanova: What a lovely night, I couldn't be more mirthfully.

(As they eat their meal, Bachelor looks over at Casanova with a smile)

Bachelor: You know, I never thought I'd end up having a twin brother, that has been much of a player; furthermore, one who has been completely contrary to me.

Casanova: Hey, I'm not that bad anymore.

Bachelor: Sure, sure. Just wait until I dig up dirt on you.

(They all laugh.)

Precious: These two used to chase over the same women, look at even our countenance Grace, it is similar; they have the same predilection and inclination.

Grace: *(Smiling.)*I can attest to that.

(they all laugh.)

Casanova: Do you remember when we were in grade 9, being summoned at the Principal's office for writing love letters to the same girl, and she responded to us both? *(There is laughter on the table.)*

Bachelor: I remember that day. It was embarrassing and laughable.

Grace: *(curious)* . What happened?

Bachelor: We had to read those letters in front of the whole class. Casanova started and I followed, and she had to read both; she went tears.

(They all laugh.)

Precious: I remember, I was in Grade 8; we were looking all over the windows.

Bachelor :(*feeling his heart overflowing with love and gratitude to the surrounding people.)*

Bachelor :(*Elated.)* I have to say, this is such a lovely night. Being here with you all, enjoying good food, drinks, and each other's company just feels so perfect. The soft glow of the candles, the warm atmosphere of the restaurant, and the pleasant chill of the autumn breeze outside all make this moment so magical.

Bachelor :(*Touched by Grace, his girlfriend, who sat beside him, holding his hand and gazing into his eyes with* affection.)

Bachelor: And being here with you, Grace, just makes everything even more special. I feel so grateful to have you in my life, to hold your hand, look into your beautiful eyes, and share this moment with you. You make my heart sing, and every moment with you is like a dream come true. I love you. I feel such a rush of warmth in my chest and a deep sense of contentment to share this moment with you.

(Grace is captivated and affectionate, with almost tears on her face; Precious gives her a tissue to wipe them; she thereafter embraces and kisses with Bachelor.)

Bachelor: And Casanova, my dear twin brother, I'm glad we've come a long way from those days when we used to fight and bicker over everything. I'm grateful for that stranger who made us shake hands at the beach; appease by all that came thereafter, and for all the lessons we've learnt together. You're the only person who truly understands me, and I'm blessed to have you by my side. I love you so deeply with an unshakeable love. I thank God, for bringing us together.

(Casanova crosses over the table and hugs him, then sits back.)

Bachelor: And Precious, you're a gem. It's amazing to see how much you've grown since we were all in Fish Hoek High School. Your confidence, intelligence, and beauty are all inspiring. I'm honoured to be on this date with you and to witness the love between you and my brother.

(Precious, sits quietly, listening to Bachelor's words with a smile on her face. She could feel the affection and warmth in the air, and she was grateful to be a part of this special moment.)

Precious: Thank you very much Bachelor that was deep. *(Wiping tears, and hugging him.)*

Casanova :(*feeling such a lump form in his throat as he looks around the room at his brother, his girlfriend, and Grace.)*

Casanova: I feel such an astounding sense of warmth and love over you, Bachelor, and I know; I am so lucky to have you people in my life.

(They all sip some glass of red wine.)

Bachelor: You all make me feel complete and at ease. I love you all, with a sincere and a cleansed rinsed heart. You've filled an empty hole, and gratified all my all my human instinct. This is such an amazing, and a wonderful night. Thank you Jesus. *(They all embrace, kiss and then sit.)*

Casanova: (appeased.) Hallelujah! I couldn't agree more Bachelor. *(His voice choked with emotion.)* Tonight has been truly special, and I am so grateful to be sharing it with all of you. It's amazing to think that we used to hate each other, and now here we are, having the time of our lives.

(He looks at his girlfriend, Precious, and feels a surge of affection for her; she smiles back at him, and he feels his heart being swell with love.)

Casanova: *(Gratitude.)* I know you are the one for me, and I feel so blessed to have you and have found you. I am sorry for all the trouble I have caused you; apologise to you and Grace-for all the girls-the women I have hurt because of my lustfulness and self-enrichment embedded in self-centredness. I love you so deeply, with such unshakeable incomparable love. I could be nowhere else than with you. *(Precious embraces and kisses with him.)*

(He looks back at his brother and Grace, feels deep affection.)

Casanova: *(Voice cracking with emotions.)* Bachelor, I am overwhelmed with a sense of deep gratitude and affection for you and Grace. I know you shall always be there for me through thick and thin. The strong bond we have is such a luck and a blessing to have. I am blessed and lucky to be with you all. I love you Bachelor with a steadfast anchoring love. *(Bachelor, immersed with affection, emotion and love, crosses over, embraces and kisses with him.)*

Casanova: Let's make a toast guys.

(They raise their red wine glasses up the table.)

Casanova: I love you all, with such high sincerity and an eased contempt clean heart. *(He embraces with Precious, then with Grace.)*

Casanova: *(Sighs.)* Tonight has been one of the best nights of my life, and I will never forget it.*(Bachelor and Casanova embrace.)* What an unprecedented love! To God alone be the glory.

(The couples laugh and chat as they leave the restaurant, the autumn night air refreshing against their skin. The city lights twinkle in them as they walk hand in hand, grateful for the unexpected bond that has brought them
together.)

The End

8 Exploring the Complexities of Conflict: An In-depth Analysis of "The Sweet Wretchedness of Love"

IN THE, "THE SWEET Wretchedness of Love," the characters grapple with a myriad of conflicts that shape their journeys and test their relationships. These conflicts can be categorized into external conflicts, which involve clashes with other characters or external forces, and internal conflicts, which are battles within the characters' own hearts and minds. Let's explore these conflicts on how they play out.

8.1 Internal Conflicts:

8.1.1 Bachelor

BACHELOR FACES INTERNAL conflicts as he navigates relationships and adulthood in the midst of the business world. He struggles with self-doubt and wrestles with societal expectations of masculinity, including patterns of sexism, infidelity, and womanizing. The conflicting notions of what is considered normal for a teenage boy further contribute to Bachelor's internal turmoil. His internal conflict explodes, whereby he addresses Casanova with certainty and boldness. At first, he yearns for a lost father figure in his life, and wonders how life could have been if his father was still alive, moreover he realises that Valentine is there to show him a father figure in his life, as he grooms him with economic, business, romantic and social life skills.

8.1.2 Casanova

CASANOVA, TOO, EXPERIENCES an internal conflict as he
realizes the emptiness of his frivolous lifestyle of playing with women and indulging in endless parties. He yearns to fix things with Precious, seeking a more meaningful and authentic connection. His rivalry with Bachelor, and Bachelor's confrontation of him, gives a heart beat, thereafter, he is in intense affliction, envy, lost in thought-questioning and challenging himself about his futile leverage lifestyle. It is his reconciliation with Bachelor calms which his inner being.

8.1.3 Valentine

VALENTINE'S INTERNAL conflict arises as he delves into the past to uncover the truth about Bachelor's lost twin brother, only to discover that Casanova is his own twin. This revelation triggers a deep-seated anger towards Helen, Casanova's adoptive stepmother, for concealing the illegal adoption. Valentine grapples with conflicting emotions and a sense of betrayal.

8.1.4 Cynthia

CYNTHIA, GRAPPLES WITH internal conflicts that deeply impact her personal life and relationships. At the core of her struggles lie insecurities and fears that have shaped her perceptions and actions. One significant internal conflict Cynthia faces revolves around her relationship with Charles, her boyfriend. Insecurities plague her thoughts, leading her to question her worthiness of love and commitment. These insecurities manifest in her reluctance to accept Bachelor's romantic interest in her sister, Precious. Cynthia's fear of losing Charles and her desire to protect her relationship contribute to her hesitance, as she believes that Bachelor's involvement with Precious would threaten the stability of her own connection with Charles.

Furthermore, in her quest to protect her relationship with Charles, Cynthia grapples with the internal conflict of whether to reveal the truth about Andrews' unfaithfulness to Charles' mother. She discovers the unsettling reality that Andrews has been cheating on his wife, creating a moral dilemma within Cynthia. On one hand, she feels compelled to disclose the truth to Charles, believing that he deserves to know the reality of his father's actions. On the other hand, she fears the potential consequences of revealing the painful truth, as it may shatter Charles' perception of his family and further strain their relationship.

8.2 External CONFLICTS

8.2.1 Bachelor and Casanova

ONE PROMINENT EXTERNAL conflict revolves around Bachelor and Casanova, whose rivalry over Precious fuels tension throughout the play. Their differing views on how to treat women and what it means to be a man create a rift between them, with Bachelor challenging Casanova's lifestyle of manipulation and deceit. As Bachelor exposes Casanova's secrets, their relationship becomes strained, and Casanova's girlfriends, including Precious, Ntombi, Rose, and Amanda, find themselves embroiled in bitterness and frustration. The girls, too, engage in conflicts among themselves, resulting in fights and animosity.

In all, the Sweet Wretchedness of Love portrays a web of conflicts that intertwine the lives of its characters, adding depth and tension to the story. The main external conflict revolves around

Bachelor and Casanova, two friends turned rivals, as they vie for the affections of Precious. Their clash stems from their differing views on how to treat women and the meaning of masculinity. Bachelor, driven by a desire for genuine love and connection, challenges Casanova's womanizing ways, exposing his secrets and lies. This revelation infuriates Casanova and creates a bitter rift between them.

8.2.2 Clashes Between Girls and Casanova

As the conflicts extend to the women involved with Casanova. Precious, Ntombi, Rose, and Amanda all become entangled in bitterness and disappointment as they discover the truth about Casanova's manipulations. The girls find themselves pitted against each other, with tensions rising between Rose and Precious, as well as Rose and Amanda, particularly during confrontations at False Bay College. Ultimately, Casanova's actions lead him to choose Precious, causing a rupture in his relationships with the other women.

8.2.3 Bachelor and Cynthia

FURTHER CONFLICTS ARISE when Cynthia, Precious's sister, objects to Bachelor dating her sibling, given his close friendship with her boyfriend, Charles. Cynthia's opposition sparks conflict between her and Bachelor, while Charles finds himself in a hostile confrontation with his father, Andrews, due to his father's infidelity.

8.2.4 Juxtaposition

These conflicts of love, betrayal, loyalty, and self-discovery drive the narrative of "The Sweet Wretchedness of Love," showcasing the complexities and challenges faced by its characters as they navigate

relationships, personal growth, and the consequences of their choices.

8.3 Conclusion: The Tapestry of Conflicts in "The Sweet Wretchedness of Love"

"THE SWEET WRETCHEDNESS of Love" weaves a captivating tapestry of internal and external conflicts, portraying the intricate struggles faced by its diverse cast of characters. From the external conflicts of rivalry, secrets, and infidelity to the internal conflicts of self-doubt, identity, and moral dilemmas, the play immerses readers in a world where relationships are tested, emotions run high, and personal growth becomes imperative.

The external conflicts within the play showcase the clashes between characters, highlighting the tensions that arise from their differing perspectives and desires. The rivalry between Bachelor and Casanova over the affections of Precious drives a central external conflict, as they battle not only for her love but also for their contrasting views on relationships and masculinity. The revelation of Casanova's hidden lifestyle and his subsequent confrontation with Bachelor adds fuel to the fire, leading to a dramatic climax.

Additionally, the conflicts involving the various romantic partners in Casanova's life—Precious, Ntombi, Rose, and Amanda—illustrate the repercussions of his actions, exposing the bitterness and frustrations that arise from his deceptive ways. The clashes between these women further intensify the external conflicts, creating a web of strained relationships and shattered trust.

Moreover, the conflicts involving Valentine, Helen, and Delilah bring forth another layer of external tensions. Valentine's pursuit of the truth about Bachelor's lost twin brother, Casanova, leads to a confrontation with Helen, who has been hiding the adoption secret.

Delilah's involvement and her blackmailing of Helen add to the complexity of these external conflicts, revealing the interconnectedness of the characters' lives.

In parallel, the internal conflicts experienced by characters like Bachelor, Casanova, and Cynthia provide a deeper exploration of their inner struggles and personal growth. Bachelor's internal conflict revolves around navigating relationships and adulthood in the midst of the business world, wrestling with societal expectations and his own insecurities. Casanova's internal conflict arises as he realizes the futility of his player lifestyle and seeks to mend his ways, particularly in his pursuit of reconciliation with Precious.

Cynthia's internal conflict showcases her insecurities, relationship struggles, and the weight of keeping secrets. Her dilemma surrounding whether to disclose Andrews' infidelity to Charles adds emotional depth to her character, as she grapples with the repercussions of her choices and the impact on her relationship with Charles.

"The Sweet Wretchedness of Love" masterfully intertwines these internal and external conflicts, immersing readers in a rich tapestry of human experiences and emotions. Through these conflicts, the play delves into themes of love, trust, self-discovery, and the complexities of navigating relationships in a world full of challenges and temptations.

As the final curtains draw, the conflicts explored in the play serve as reminders of the profound impact they have on shaping the characters' journeys and eliciting deep introspection. The conflicts become catalysts for growth, transformation, and the exploration of the human condition, leaving audiences with a poignant reflection on the highs and lows, joys and sorrows, and the complexities of love and relationships.

9 Terminology and Colloquial Language Explanation

ASGISA:

ASGISA STANDS FOR ACCELERATED and Shared Growth Initiative for South Africa. It was a South African government initiative aimed at accelerating economic growth and development in the country. The initiative was launched in 2006 with the aim of halving poverty and unemployment by 2014[1]

Supreme Court of Appeal

THIS IS WHERE SOUTH Africa's judiciary capital lies, in Bloemfontein, it is South Africa's highest court after the Constitutional Court for appeal cases from the high courts.

BRICS

AN ACRONYM FOR BRZIL, RUSSIA, China, India and South Africa; which are grouped as emerging economies, with a potential to compete with the G7 countries, which are the most advanced economies in the world.

Light Year: The distance in which light travels in a full earth year at a speed of 300 000 kilometres per second, which is equivalent to 9.4 trillion kilometres.

Virgo Supercluster : Virgo Supercluster:The Virgo Supercluster is a vast cosmic structure that contains our own Milky Way galaxy along with thousands of other galaxies. It spans over

---

1. https://omalley.nelsonmandela.org/index.php/site/q/03lv02409/04lv02410/05lv02415/ 06lv02416.htm

110 million light-years in diameter and is named after the Virgo constellation where it is predominantly located. The supercluster is a complex network of galaxy groups and clusters, creating a rich cosmic tapestry. Its immense size and gravitational interactions shape the motion of galaxies within it, playing a significant role in the large-scale structure of the universe.

Laniakea Supercluster: The Laniakea Supercluster is an even larger structure that encompasses the Virgo Supercluster and several other nearby superclusters. Laniakea, which means "immense heaven" in Hawaiian, spans over 500 million light-years in diameter and contains millions of galaxies. It was discovered in 2014 and is characterized by its gravitational influence, which determines the flow of galaxies within this vast cosmic region. The concept of Laniakea helps us better understand the distribution of matter in the universe on the largest scales and provides insights into the dynamics of galaxy clusters and superclusters.

9.1 Colloquial Language

SBWL: A Xhosa slang from the word SABWELI which means to crave, desire or yearn for something.

Isisdudu: A mixture of maize meal, with pumpkins/ butternut, it is usually made from boiled pumpkins and maize meal.

Unonkiloyi: A spiteful woman

Ndazi Uthetha Nabani: I wonder whom are speaking with.

Ayiye Madam, Asizanga kuzodlala apha: Go madam, we are not here to play!

*UPHAKATHI KWEBHAYI ne Tinarha: When you are in a dilemma, faced with difficulty to chose between two alternatives.

IBhayi *(A bay)* is a Xhosa name for the city of Port Elizabeth, Eastern Cape, South Africa which means "a bay", situated in the Agloa Bay; it was founded in 1820. Tinanarha is a Xhosa name for the town of Uitenhage, Port Elizabeth and Uitenhage are the biggest car manufacturing cities in Africa (Muller,2020)

Volkswagen, Ford, Goodyear, Bridgestone, Isuzu South Africa, Continental Tyre, Shatterprufe, and First Automotive Works (FAW) are made in Port Elizabeth-Uitenhage industrial hub (Muller,2020).

10 References:

Banham, M. (Ed.). (2014). The Cambridge Guide to Theatre (2nd ed.). Cambridge University Press.

Elam, K. (2017). The Semiotics of Theatre and Drama (3rd ed.). Routledge.

Lupton, J. (2018). Understanding Plays: Analysing Drama and Theatre. Bloomsbury Methuen Drama.

Shakespeare, W. (1987). Hamlet. The Oxford Shakespeare: Oxford University Press.

Lawrence, D.H. (1997). The Rainbow. Oxford World Classics: Oxford University Press.

Eliot, G. (1990). Selected Essays, Poems and Other Writings. Penguin Books.

Cook, E, (2008). John Keats. The Major Works Including Endymion and Selected letters. Oxford World Classics: Oxford University Press.

Gill, R. (1979). Oxford Shakespeare Julius Caesar. Oxford University Press.

Jones V. (1996). Janes Austen: Pride and Prejudice. Introduction and Notes. Penguin Books.

Lammer, A, Bursey, J and Wright, L. (1994). Shakespeare's Macbeth. The Institute for the Study of English in South Africa, Rhodes University: Macmillan.

Saunders, W. (2005). The Tragedy of Anthony and Cleopatra. Shakespeare 2000.

Saunders, W. (2005). The Twelfth Night. Shakespeare 2000.

Ionesco, E. (1950). The Bald Soprano.

Charters, A. (2017). The Story and Its Writer: An Introduction to Short Fiction (10th ed.). Bedford/St. Martin's.

Watt, I. (2019). The Rise of the Novel: Studies in Defoe, Richardson, and Fielding (3rd ed.). University of California Press.

Qangule.Z, S. (2008). Amaza.Kagiso Education.

Saule, N. (2009). Ukhozi Olumaphiko Phiko.Nasou Via Afrika.

Nkohla, M. (2014). Ngenxa Yesithembiso. Maskew Miller Longman.

Tully, R. B., et al. (2014). The Laniakea Supercluster of Galaxies. Nature, 513(7516), 71-73.

Shapley, A., et al. (2020). The Distribution and Kinematics of Warm Ionized Gas in Laniakea. The Astrophysical Journal, 893(1), 2.

Cardiomyopathy.(2022).Mayo Clinic. Available at:https://www.mayoclinic.org/diseases-conditions/ broken-heart-syndrome/symptoms-causes/syc-20354617   [Accessed: 2023, June 01]

[1]

Don't miss out!

Visit the website below and you can sign up to receive emails whenever SIYA MANCI publishes a new book. There's no charge and no obligation.

https://books2read.com/r/B-A-BVZZ-WFXMC

BOOKS 2 READ

Connecting independent readers to independent writers.

Milton Keynes UK
Ingram Content Group UK Ltd.
UKHW020636140923
428670UK00014B/618